For Miro Demian

ISBN 0-590-69822-2

Copyright © 1991 by Nord-Süd Verlag AG, Gossau Zürich, Switzerland.
First published in Switzerland under the title Hoppel.
English translation copyright © 1991 by North-South Books, Inc.
All rights reserved. Published by Scholastic Inc., 555 Broadway, New York,
NY 10012, by arrangement with North-South Books, Inc.

24 23 22 21 20 19 18 17 16 15 14 13 14 0/0 1 2 3 4 5/0

Printed in the U.S.A.

First Scholastic printing, January 1996

HOPPER

By Marcus Pfister

SCHOLASTIC INC.
New York Toronto London Auckland Sydney

"Wake up, Hopper!"

Mama gently pushed him with her nose. Hopper opened his eyes slowly and stretched himself.

"Do I have to wash myself again, Mama?"

"You ask the same question every day, Hopper. Don't you want your fur to stay white and healthy? Wash yourself and then you can play with your friend."

Hopper slowly licked his fur, starting with his paws.

He was a beautiful hare. His fur was pure white, like his mother's, but the tip of one of his ears was blue, which was very unusual.

When he had finished cleaning himself he ran over to Nick, who was still sleeping soundly under a bush.

Hopper tickled his nose and tapped his ears. But when Nick refused to wake up, Hopper just pulled him out from under the bush.

"What's going on?" muttered Nick sleepily. He tried to push Hopper away and soon the two started wrestling.

They made so much noise rolling around and laughing that the hedgehog woke up from hibernation. "Hey! Stop that noise!" he yelled. "I still have a month left to sleep."

"Sorry," said Nick softly. "We didn't realize you were there."

Wrestling in the snow had made Hopper hungry. "What is there to eat?" he asked his mother who was hopping by.

"Let's look for food together," said his mother.

"But I'd rather stay with Nick and play," Hopper said reluctantly. "Please bring me something."

"Come on now, don't be lazy," she said. "You can play with Nick tomorrow." So Hopper said goodbye to his friend and sullenly hopped away.

"Mama, wait! My paws are freezing. The snow is so cold."

"I know it's cold, but it's also white like we are so it's easier for us to hide from other animals."

"But why does it snow, Mama?"

"Most of the plants, bushes and grass have to rest in winter. When the snow melts in the spring it turns into water that helps them grow."

"Why do they need to rest?" asked Hopper, lying down in the snow. "They don't have to jump through the cold snow to look for food. I want to rest, too."

Suddenly Mama looked up and saw a falcon swooping down at them.

"Run!" she screamed. "Run as fast as you can to the forest and hide in the bushes!"

Hopper bounded away and his mother ran back and forth across the field to distract the falcon.

"Goodness, that was close," Mama sighed as the falcon flew away.

"What did that flying hare want?" asked Hopper.

"That was *not* a hare," she said sternly. "That was a falcon. I've warned you about falcons before. They love to grab little hares like you. That's why I've been trying to teach to you how to run back and forth across the open fields."

"But how could he see us? He was flying so high in the sky."

"Falcons have very strong eyes," his mother replied. "They're as dangerous as foxes. Come on, let's run back across the field."

Hopper tried to follow his mother, but when he turned too quickly he tumbled in the snow.

"Don't worry," said his mother. "You just need to keep trying. It wasn't easy for me to learn either."

Then the two of them went to look for food again.

Suddenly, Hopper came out of a bush, screaming, "Mama, a tree on four legs is after me."

His mother just laughed. "That's not a tree, that's a stag."

"A stag," Hopper repeated thoughtfully. "Will his branches grow leaves in the spring?"

"Those aren't branches," said his mother patiently. "Those are called antlers."

"And what does a stag need antlers for, Mama?"

"To defend himself against his enemies. And when he is hungry he uses them to dig in the ground to find food."

"I wish I had antlers," Hopper said quickly. "I'm starving."

"Here we are," said his mother. "This bark is very tasty."

"I don't like it," said Hopper, frowning. "It's so wet and cold. I'd rather eat some berries."

"There won't be berries until spring," she said, "so eat your bark like a good boy."

When the two of them were full they started to hop back
home. The sun was going down and soon it would be dark.

"How far is it, Mama?" asked Hopper. "Will we be there
soon? I'm tired."

"Don't worry, it's not far."

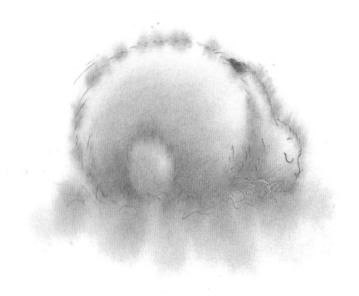

By the time they got home, the moon had come out and the stars were twinkling.

"Will the snow go away?" Hopper asked as he lay down.

"Yes," Mama said, as she gently stroked his back. "In spring, when the sun gets warmer, the snow will melt. Then the flowers will bloom in the fields and the leaves will grow on the trees. Farmers will plant their crops and we can search for carrots and lettuce. Would you like that?"

Hopper didn't say anything. He had already fallen asleep, dreaming of spring and juicy red berries.

CONVERSE® ALL STAR™
SOCCER
HOW TO PLAY LIKE A PRO

A MOUNTAIN LION BOOK

John Wiley & Sons, Inc.
New York • Chichester • Weinheim • Brisbane • Singapore • Toronto

This text is printed on acid-free paper.

Copyright © 1997 by Mountain Lion, Inc.
Published by John Wiley & Sons, Inc.

In order to keep the instructions in this book as simple as possible, the word "he" is used to mean either boys or girls.

The publisher and the author have made every reasonable effort to insure that the activities in the book are safe when conducted as instructed but assume no responsibility for any damage caused or sustained while performing the activities in this book. Parents, guardians, and/or coaches should supervise young readers who undertake the activities in this book.

Library of Congress Cataloging-in-Publication Data

Converse all star soccer : how to play like a pro.
    p. cm. — (Converse all star sports series)
   "A Mountain Lion book."
   ISBN 0-471-15992-1 (alk. paper)
   1. Soccer—Training I. Converse (Firm) II. Series.
GV943.9.T7C588 1997
796.334—dc20   96-39054

Printed in the United States of America
10 9 8 7 6 5 4 3 2 1

CONTENTS

Soccer is a graceful game of skill and ability. Play the game, and you'll be hooked before the first goal is scored. No wonder that soccer is the most popular team sport in the world.

Games that used goal lines and passing a ball were played in 400 B.C. in China, and in A.D. 200, in Rome. During the Middle Ages, adults and children played a form of soccer in the streets of London, England. Team size depended on how many people wanted to play—sometimes entire towns participated. Different groups used different rules. Soccer became so popular that during the reign of King Edward III, the game was outlawed because it took time away from the soldiers' military duties!

In 1848, the first set of rules were written down. The game was called association football, but it was soon shortened to just "football." Football spread throughout the world, and became very popular in Europe and South America. As rugby football and American football became popular, the sport went back to being called association football. That was a mouthful, so it got shortened to "assoc" and then changed to "soccer." The name, soccer, stuck in the United States, but most other countries still call it football.

In 1913 the Federation of International Football Associations (FIFA) was formed to link all the soccer teams together and make sure that everyone was playing the same game. The FIFA started the World Cup Competitions to decide the best soccer team in the world. The first World Cup was held in 1930, in Montevideo, Uruguay, South America. It has been held every four years since (except for during World War II), with players from over 140 countries competing.

In the United States, soccer has moved a bit slower. From 1968 to 1985 there was a professional league, called the North American Soccer League (NASL), but there weren't enough fans to support the teams. In 1994, the World Cup was held in the United States for the first time. Now Americans are playing soccer. High schools and colleges have soccer programs, youth leagues are everywhere, and U.S. soccer teams take part in international competition.

The chapters in this book tell you how to learn the skills you need to play soccer. This book also gives you the rules of the game, ways to win, and tips on training. Keep reading to find out how to play soccer like a pro.

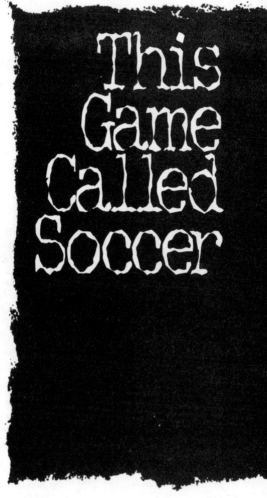

CHAPTER 1

This Game Called Soccer

Soccer is fast and exciting. The players are always moving, and you can never be sure just what's going to happen next. Soccer is a simple game. The action is easy to follow, and the rules are easy to understand. Best of all, soccer is a game for boys and girls of all ages and sizes. You aren't too tall to play soccer, or too short. Every player on the team gets plenty of chances to handle the ball during the game.

Getting Started

To play soccer, you need a few players, an open area, and a ball. You also need to know a little about the game.

The Aim of the Game
Two teams of 11 players each try to move the ball down the field, across the goal line, and into the other team's goal. The team with the most goals at the end of the game is the winner.

Get the Team Spirit!

Soccer players are members of a *team*. Players have to work together to make as many goals as they can for their team. To keep the team spirit, you have to play for the good of your team instead of trying to be a superstar.

The Ball

The ball is round and made of real or fake leather tiles (pieces) that are stitched together. The ball is 27 to 28 inches around the middle and weighs 14 to 16 ounces. It is filled with air so it will bounce.

The Field

Soccer fields are not all the same size. The length has to be between 100 yards and 120 yards. The field can't be wider than it is long. The lines at the ends of the field are called *endlines* and the lines on the sides of the field are called *sidelines*. Each corner of the field is marked with a flag or a plastic cone.

The length of the field is divided in half by the *center line*. In the middle of the field is a *center circle* that is 10 yards in diameter. In the middle of the center circle is a *center spot*.

At each end of the field is a goal that is eight feet high by 24 feet wide. The goal is made of a wood or metal famework that is covered with nets which are staked to the ground so that the ball can't slip out the back or sides. The part of the endline that runs across the front of the goal is called the *goal line*.

In front of each goal is a six yard by 20 yard area, called the *goal area*. Beyond the goal area is another rectangle that is 44 yards by 18 yards, called the *penalty box*. Inside the penalty box is a *penalty spot* which is opposite the center of the goal and 12 yards from the goal line.

1-1: To score a goal, the offensive player has to put the ball between the two side posts and under the crossbar. Accurate shooting is important so it's always helpful to practice as much as you can.

Scoring

To count as a goal, the whole ball must pass over the opponent's whole goal line and into the *goalmouth* (the wide opening of the nets) (Figure 1-1).

Uniforms

Uniforms are made up of shorts, shirt, calf-length socks, and shoes that usually have rubber cleats (bumps on the bottom that keep the shoes from slipping). Some players also wear shin guards.

Timing

An official game has two 45 minute halves with a five-minute rest period between halves. Youth league soccer may have shorter halves. During play, the clock keeps running, except when a player is injured or when a technical problem is called by the referee. The game ends with a final whistle, even if the score is tied. If a championship match ends in a tie, an extra period, called an *overtime*, is played. In an official FIFA game the overtime is divided into two 15 minute periods.

1-2: The goalkeeper is positioned to stop any balls from entering the goal. Sometimes, it takes an acrobatic save to prevent a goal.

Offense and Defense

When your team has the ball, then you are playing *offense* and your team is the *attacking* team. While playing offense, your team's job is to score a goal.

When the other team has the ball, then you are playing *defense* and your team is the *defending* team. While playing defense, your team's job is to stop the other team from scoring a goal, and to steal the ball from them.

The Players

Each team has 11 players on the field at one time. When you are on a soccer team, you play one of the four basic positions:

- The *fullbacks* (also called defenders), defend their team's goal from attack and steal the ball from the attackers.

- The main job of the *forwards* is to shoot the ball into the goal.

- The *midfielders* (also called halfbacks), are the links between the fullbacks and the forwards. Midfielders coordinate the play by moving up, down, and across the field, sometimes attacking, sometimes defending, depending on how they are needed.

- The *goalkeeper* (also called a goalie), guards his team's goal. He is the only player who can use his hands to catch the ball (Figure 1-2).

The fullbacks, midfielders, and forwards are called *field players* because they play on the field. The number of field players in each position can change, depending on the play of the game.

The goalkeeper usually plays at the goal and wears a different uniform than the field players. The goalkeeper can also play on the rest of the field, and while he does, he is a field player and cannot use his hands and arms on the ball.

Playing the Game

The game begins with a *kickoff* in the center circle. For a kickoff, the ball is placed on the center spot, the referee blows the whistle, and the kicking team starts the play by kicking the ball forward, toward the opponent's goal. The player who makes the first kick is not allowed to touch the ball again until another player has touched it.

During a kickoff, both teams must stay on their defensive halves of the field (the half with their goal) until the ball is touched. The defending team must also remain outside the center circle.

A coin toss decides which team kicks off first. The team that does not kick off the first half will kick off the second half. There's also a kickoff after each goal is scored.

Moving the Ball

The ball is moved down the field by any part of the body except the arms and hands, from the shoulders to the fingertips.

Juggling Drill

Juggling means keeping the soccer ball up in the air by using any part of your body except your arms and hands (Figure 1-3). When

1-3: Soccer players should always practice their juggling. It's the best way to improve ball skills and develop good "touch" with your feet. Juggling can be praticed alone or with a teammate.

you learn to juggle, you learn some of the ball handling skills that you need to play in a game. Start the drill by raising one foot a couple of inches off the ground, while keeping your foot level. Drop the ball on your instep (the top of your foot that is covered by your shoelaces) and use your foot to bounce the ball back up in the air. When the ball comes down, bounce it up again with your instep. Bounce it up as many times as you can without letting it touch the ground.

To juggle with your thigh, bend one knee and raise it so your thigh is level with the ground. Drop the ball on your thigh and raise your knee to bounce the ball back up in the air. When the ball comes down, bounce it up again with your thigh.

To juggle with your head, toss the ball above your head. When it comes down, bend your knees, raise your heels a little off the ground, tip your head back, and use your forehead to send the ball back up in the air.

Practice juggle using both feet, both thighs, your head, and even your chest. See if you can bounce the ball from one part of your body to another without letting it touch the ground. Once you can juggle while standing still, try it while walking forward.

The Rules

Some important rules of soccer are:

Out of Bounds

If the ball goes over the sideline, it is *out of bounds* and is put back in play by a *throw-in*. The ball is thrown in bounds at the spot where it left the field by a member of the team that did not touch it last. The ball is thrown with two hands; the arms must come straight over the head, and both feet must be touching the ground. A throw-in is the only time a field player can use his hands on the ball.

1-4: A corner kick can be a dangerous offensive weapon for a team's offense. Many goals are scored as a result of well-placed corner kicks.

If the ball goes out of bounds over the endline, it is put back into play by a kick. If the attacking team kicked it out over the defending team's goal line, then the defending team gets a *goal kick*. For a goal kick, the ball is placed inside the goal area on the same side that it went out of bounds. Attacking team members may not be inside the penalty area when the kick is taken. Any player on the defending team may kick the ball, which must leave the penalty box before another player can touch it.

If the ball is kicked out of bounds by a defensive player, the attacking team gets a *corner kick*. For a corner kick, the ball is placed in the corner of the field on the same side that it went out of bounds. All defending players must be 10 yards away from the ball until it is kicked (Figure 1-4).

Fouls

When a player breaks a rule in a soccer game, it's called a *foul*, or *violation*. Some fouls in soccer include: kicking, tripping, charging, striking, holding, or pushing an opponent. It is also a foul if a field player touches the ball with his hand or arm.

When a player makes a foul, the other team is awarded a *direct free kick* on the goal. Direct means that the ball can be shot straight into the goal for a score without being touched by another player. Free means that the player gets to kick the ball without interference from the other team. On a direct free kick, the ball is placed where the foul occurred. Members of the team making the kick can stand as close to the ball as they like, but members of the defending team must be at least 10 yards away from the ball. The kicker may *boot* (kick) the ball in any direction, but the ball must travel at least 27 inches before it is in play.

If the foul is committed by the defending team inside its own penalty box, then the attacking team gets a *penalty kick*. The penalty kick is taken from the penalty spot, directly in front of the goal. A penalty kick is a one-on-one contest between any player on the offensive team and the defending team's goalie. Penalty kicks often make a goal.

There are a few other fouls that call for a different penalty. These fouls include:

- *Dangerous play*, which can cause injuries, such as *high kicking* (kicking the ball above chest height).

- *Obstruction*, which means blocking an opponent's path.

- *Poor conduct*, such as waving your hands in an opponent's face, kicking the ball out of bounds on purpose, or fighting with an opponent.

The penalty for the above violations is an *indirect free kick*. An *indirect kick* means that the ball may not go into the goal until it has touched another player. The ball is placed at the location of the foul and opponents must stay 10 yards from the ball until it has been put into play.

Offside Rule

Except for the goalie, players are allowed to move almost anywhere on the field. The one exception to this rule is called *offside*. A player must always keep either the ball or two opponents (one can be the goalie) between himself and the goal. This rule was made to keep players from hanging out near the goal, waiting for a long kick to come to them. Offside is usually not called by the referee when a player just happens to be in an offside position and doesn't get in the way of the flow of the game. You can not be offside on a corner kick, goal kick, or throw-in.

The Officials

There are usually three officials at a soccer game, a *referee* and two *linespeople* (Figure 1-5). The referee is in charge of the field and uses a whistle to start and stop the play. He enforces the rules, calls penalties, and acts as the official timekeeper. The linespeople stay on each sideline and use flags to show when a ball is out of bounds, and which team gets the corner kick, goal kick, or throw-in.

1-5: The referee calls fouls and whistles for play to be stopped when the ball goes out of bounds. Good players should always respect the referee and never question his calls.

1-6: Always be on your toes in the game of soccer. Though speed and skill are very important, hustle and desire play a major role as well.

The Coach

The coach is really a teacher. His job is to teach his players how to play the game and show them how they can improve their skills. The coach plans the strategy (game plan) for each game.

Make It Up, Play It Out

Here's two juggling games you can play with your friends.

Group Juggling

You need three or more players, a soccer ball, and a small playing area. Players stand in a small circle. One player tosses the ball to the next player in the circle, who juggles the ball as long as he wants (can be only one juggle), then bounces it to the next player. The game goes on until the ball hits the ground. The player who drops the ball is out. The last player still juggling the ball is the winner.

Hunter

You need three or more players, a soccer ball for every player except one, and a playing area. All the players except for one have a ball, and they begin juggling them. The player without the ball (the hunter) moves among the jugglers, bothering them, but not touching them or the balls. As soon as one of the jugglers loses the ball, the hunter tries to get the ball. If he gets it, he begins juggling and the player who lost it becomes the hunter.

1. To count as a goal, the whole ball must pass over the opponent's whole goal line and into the goalmouth.
2. When your team has the ball, your team members are the attackers.
3. When the other team has the ball, your team members are the defensive players.
4. The fullbacks defend the goal, the forwards shoot the ball into the goal, and the midfielders are the links between the fullbacks and the forwards.
5. The game begins with a kickoff in the center circle.
6. There is a kickoff after each goal is scored.
7. When the ball goes out of bounds over the sideline, it is put back into play by a throw-in. This is the only time that a field player can use his hands on the ball.
8. When a player breaks a rule it's called a foul and his team gets a penalty.

CHAPTER 2

Training to Play

Before you can play any sport, you need to get your body in top physical shape. For soccer, you need to develop quickness and build strength and *endurance* (the ability to keep going a long time). This is what training sessions are all about. Before you begin a training session, you need to warm up (loosen) your body. To do this, take a quick jog around the field, then stretch.

Stretching

Stretching your muscles makes you more flexible (able to move easily) and makes it less likely that you will be hurt during practice or during a game. (Since you never want to stretch a cold muscle, make sure you take that jog around the field first to warm up.)

When you stretch, keep your body relaxed and take long, slow breaths. Stretching should feel good. Hold each stretch for at least thirty seconds and don't stretch so far that you feel pain. If stretching is painful, stop the stretch and get advice from your coach.

When you play soccer, you use your whole body, so you need to stretch all the muscle groups. A good way to do this is to start with your feet and work your way up to your head.

Lower Leg Stretching

While standing up, lift one foot off the ground. Hold you leg still and move your foot in a circle while you count to eight (Figure 2-1). This will loosen up your ankle. Now do the same with the other foot.

The next two stretches are for the backs of your calves and your Achilles tendons. Keep your feet flat on the ground. Bend over until your hands touch the ground in front of you. "Walk" your hands out in front of you until you feel your heels start to lift up off the ground. Let one heel come up and keep the other one flat on the ground; you'll feel a good stretch up the back of the calf on the leg with the heel still on the ground. Now bend your knee a little on the leg you are stretching and you will feel the stretch in your Achilles tendon. Now lift the heel of the stretched leg, put your other heel flat on the ground, and repeat the stretch with the other leg.

2-1: Balance yourself on one leg, hold the opposite leg out, and move your foot around in a circular motion. Do this three times for ten seconds, and then switch to the other leg.

Upper Leg Stretching

While standing up, lift one foot up behind you and grab the ankle. Now push your foot out away from your hand until you feel a stretch down the front of your thigh. Count to five, then change legs and stretch the front of the other thigh (Figure 2-2). If you have trouble keeping your balance during this stretch, look at a spot on the ground about six feet in front of you and balancing will be easier.

To stretch the back of the thigh, stand with your feet crossed, flat on the ground. Bend your knees a little and bend over, trying to touch your toes with your fingertips. Hold the stretch while you count to five. Switch the position of your feet and repeat the stretch.

2-2: Balance yourself on one leg, and pull the other leg back so your heel touches your rear end. You should feel a stretch in your upper thigh.

Middle Body Stretching

The hip flexor muscle runs from the top of your thigh to your trunk (the body, not including arms and legs). To stretch the hip flexor, bend your knees and place both hands flat on the ground in front of you. Keep your right leg bent with the foot flat on the ground. Stretch your left leg straight out behind you, resting on the toes. Squeeze your butt and press your left hip toward the ground. You will feel the stretch in your hip flexor. Now shift your position to stretch the inside of your left thigh. Turn your body to the left. Keep your left leg straight, but turn it so your knee is facing up to the sky. Walk your hands around to the left side as you shift position. Your toes come off the ground and your left foot rests on the heel. Feel the stretch on the inside of your left thigh. Now straighten up, change legs and do both the hip flexor and the inner thigh stretch for your right leg.

To stretch the outside of your hips, sit on the ground. Keep your right leg straight out in front of you. Cross your left leg over your right. Bend your left knee and place your left foot flat on the ground next to your right leg. Turn your body so that your head, shoulders, and stomach are facing to the left. Grab your left knee with your arms and pull it into your body. You will feel the stretch in your left hip. Repeat the stretch on the other side.

2-3: Make sure you stretch out the upper body along with the lower body. This exercise will loosen up the shoulders.

To stretch your groin, sit on the ground, bend your knees and bring the soles of your feet together. Your knees will be bent out to the sides and your feet will be right in front of your body. Press your knees toward the ground, and feel the stretch in your groin.

To stretch your waist and your sides, sit on the ground with your legs crossed in front of you. Lay your right arm across your lap so your fingers are pointing to the left, palm facing up. Bring your left arm above your head with your elbow bent so your fingers are pointing to the right. Without leaning forward, bend your body to the right so your right ear is parallel to the ground. Feel the stretch in your left side. Switch the position of your arms and repeat the stretch on the other side.

Shoulder and Arm Stretching

To stretch your shoulders, start from a standing position. Stick your right arm straight out in front of you, then move it in across your body so the fingers are pointing to the left. Keep your right arm straight and grab your right elbow with your left hand. Pull your right arm close to your body until you feel the stretch in your right shoulder (Figure 2-3). Hold the stretch while you count to five. Repeat the stretch on the other side.

To stretch the triceps muscle (back of the arm), raise your right arm straight up into the air. Bend your right elbow so that your hand drops down behind your head and touches your left shoulder blade. Use your left hand to grab the right elbow and gently pull the right elbow toward the back of your head (Figure 2-4). You will feel the stretch in the back of your right arm. Hold the stretch while you count to five. Switch the positions of your arms and repeat the stretch on the other side.

2-4: You need to pump your arms to run fast, which means they need to be as loose as your legs. Stretch your tricep muscles by pulling you elbow back behind your head.

Neck Stretching

To stretch your neck muscles, start from a standing or sitting position. Bend your neck to the right and press your right ear toward your right shoulder (Figure 2-5). Hold the stretch for a few seconds, then repeat the stretch on the other side. Turn your head slowly to the right as far as you can without causing pain.

2-5: Stretch your neck muslces out so you can get power behind your headballs.

Bring your head back to the center and turn it to the left. Repeat five times to each side.

To strengthen your neck muscles after you have stretched them, lock your hands together in front of you by lacing your fingers. Place them on your forehead and press backward as you use your neck muscles to press forward. Continue pressing your head against your hands for about 10 seconds. Repeat this exercise two more times.

Endurance Training

When you play soccer, you must have the ability to run nonstop for 45 minutes with a high level of energy. The best way to train for endurance is by taking a long run. Be sure to warm up and stretch before starting your long run. On your first long run, you should run as far as you can until you get tired and out of breath. Stop running if you have pain anywhere in your body. Each time you run, try to run a little farther until you can run at least five miles without getting very tired or very out of breath. Five miles is about the distance you will need to run during a soccer game.

Many coaches have their players do some long distance running at the beginning of each practice, but they can't make the runs very long without using up too much of the practice time. That's why it's so important for you to do some long distance running on your own. If you run five miles, three times a week, you'll have great endurance during a game.

2-6

2-6: You have to be in great shape to be a good soccer player. Sprints and running for distance are an absolute necessity in your training. You can't show off your great skills if you're bent over gasping for air.

Circuit Training

You can build up endurance and develop your ball handling skills at the same time by doing *circuits* (Figure 2-6). A circuit is a series of different exercises (usually about eight), one right after the other, at different places on the field.

Each player (or group of players) starts at a different point on the field. One person acts as a timer and blows a whistle every two minutes to let the players know when to move to a different spot on the field for the next exercise. The circuit ends when all the players have done all the exercises.

There are lots of good circuit exercises. Some are mostly for fitness and some are for improving ball handling. Here's a list of some exercises that are good for circuits:

2-7: A stronger player is a better player. Ball push-ups help build muscle in the arms and upper body.

1. Juggle the ball.

2. Sprint through cones while dribbling (learn how to dribble in Chapter 3).

3. Jump back and forth over the ball.

4. Sit down, throw the ball in the air, stand up, and catch it.

5. Dribble across the field and back.

6. Juggle with your head.

7. Do push-ups with your hands on the ball instead of on the ground.

8. Lie on your back and roll the ball back and forth under your body.

Strength Training

In order to be a good soccer player you need to build strength, especially in your legs, back, and stomach. One way to build strength is weightlifting. Young players, under the age of 14, probably shouldn't lift weights or use weight machines. When you do work with weights, it's important to have an expert teach you the correct way to lift.

Besides weight training, there are several drills that will help you build muscle. Some of these drills use a ball and teach your body and brain the way the ball feels and moves (Figure 2-7).

2-8: Hold the ball between your feet with your legs bent and do sit-ups. This is an excellent exercise for your upper abdominal muscles.

Crunch Drill

The crunch drill is a kind of sit-up exercise that is great for developing a soccer (strong) stomach. Lie flat on your back on the ground with your knees bent. Hold a soccer ball between your feet. Keep your knees bent and raise the ball about six inches off the ground. Sit up and bring your forehead as far forward toward the ball as you can. Repeat five times (Figure 2-8).

Leg Push Drill

The leg push is a two-person drill that will tighten your and your partner's stomach muscles. Lie down on your back on the ground. Your partner stands with one foot on either side of your head. Grab your partner's ankles and lift your legs up so they are vertical (at a 90 degree angle to the ground). Your partner grabs your ankles and gently pushes your legs back toward the ground while you try to keep them straight and off the ground. After 10 pushes, change places with your partner and repeat the drill (Figures 2-9 and 2-10).

The Rocker Drill

To strengthen your back, lie on the ground on your stomach. Keep your legs straight out behind you and your arms straight out in front of you with a soccer ball in your hands. Make your body very stiff, raise your feet and hands off the ground, and rock forward and backward on your stomach, eight times.

2-9, 2-10: Lie flat on your back and raise both legs up to your partner who is standing behind you. Grab on to his ankles to hold yourself in position. He should throw your legs forward as hard as possible while it's your job to stop them before they hit the ground. This exercise helps strengthen the upper abdominals.

Hill Sprint Drill

The quadricep muscles (along the tops of your thighs), need to be strong in order for you to be able to kick hard in a soccer game. When you run up a hill, your quad muscles get a good workout. If you can find a steep hill, sprint up it at top speed, 10 times, three times a week.

Brain Training

Playing soccer exercises your brain as well as your muscles. During a game you will feel many emotions: pressure to play well, fear of making a mistake, worry about winning, and excitement when your team scores a goal. That's why training your mind is just as important as training your body. The best way to train your mind is to always use part of each training session for just playing the game. And while you're playing, pretend it's a real game. Be just as aggressive and smart in practice as you would in a real game.

Make It Up, Play It Out

Here's two games that will keep your body in top condition and help you gain strength.

Stomach Toss

You need two or more players, one soccer ball, and a playing area. Players choose a partner, and both players lie down on their stomachs, facing each other, a few feet apart. Both players keep their legs out behind then and their arms out in front of them. They make their bodies very stiff and raise their legs and arms off the ground. Keeping legs and arms raised, they pass the ball back and forth to each other (Figure 2-11).

2-11: The stomach toss is a fun method of working the abdominal muscles. It can be practiced with two or more players.

Over Under Relay Race

You need four players on each team and a field. One player from each team stands on the endline with the three other players from his team spaced out in front of him every 10 feet. The three players, who are spaced out on the field, crouch low to the ground. On the starting signal, the player on the endline leap frogs over the three other players on his team, runs forward 10 feet and crouches down on the field. As soon as a player has been leapt over, he gets up and begins leaping over the teammates in front of him. Once all four players have leapt over all their teammates, everyone turns around and faces the other way. The first three players stand with their legs spread wide apart. The last player to finish leaping, crawls through the legs of his teammates. The first team to have all their players successfully complete the relay is the winner.

1. To play soccer, you need flexibility, strength, and endurance.
2. Warm your muscles before stretching, and stretch your muscles before training or playing.
3. Stretching should feel good. Don't forget to relax and breathe.
4. Train your mind, too, which means playing hard and smart in practice.

3

Dribbling

Fake left! Go right! Touch with your toe! Drag with your heel! Move it up! Bring it back! Ball handling, also called *dribbling*, is a lot of fancy footwork. When you dribble, you keep the ball close to your feet and push it with quick, soft kicks. While dribbling, you can move the ball forward, to the left, to the right, or backward. Use dribbling to set up a pass (kick the ball to another player) or get in position for a shot on the goal. You can also use dribbling to keep the ball away from a defensive player.

How to Dribble

When dribbling, you can use the inside, the outside, or the top of either foot to give the ball a sharp, light tap. Keep the ball close to you (within two feet) so you always have it under control and so a defensive player can't steal it. Keep your head up so you can see the other players around you and still be aware of where the ball is.

Basic Dribbling

Tap the ball forward with the inside (arch) of one foot, then use the outside of the same foot to move it forward again.

3-1: Learn to dribble with the inside of your foot first. Practice dribbling half speed, and eventually get up to full speed. Try not to kick the ball too far out in front of you.

3-2: A player has to learn to dribble with the outside of his foot as another option, and to change direction.

Take one step with your other foot, then use the first foot to move the ball again. When you tap the ball with the inside of your foot, it will tend to go off to one side. When you tap it with the outside of your foot, it will tend to go off to the other side. By using first the inside of your foot, then the outside, you can keep the ball moving forward in a straight line.

Inside-of-the-Foot Dribble

Another way to move the ball forward is to use the *inside-of-the-foot* dribble. Tap the ball forward with the inside of one foot (Figure 3-1). On your next step, tap the ball with the inside of the other foot. Keep your ankle locked (stiff) as you tap the ball about an inch above the ground. The ball should move forward in a zigzag pattern. Practice this dribble until you can move the ball forward while jogging (running slowly). Once you have mastered tapping the ball on every step, kick the ball a little harder on each tap so you can take two steps in between taps.

Use the inside-of-the-foot dribble when you need to work your way around a defensive player.

Outside-of-the Foot Dribble

Use the *outside-of-the-foot dribble* when you need to run very fast. Turn your toes in and tap the ball forward with the outside of your foot (Figure 3-2). As you move forward, always use the outside of the same foot to tap the ball. Tap the ball in the center, about an inch above the ground. Start this dribble at a walk, then as you get the hang of it, increase your speed to a jog. After you are able to jog the ball up the field easily, you're ready to try it at full speed. As you increase your speed, tap the ball ahead of you every third or fourth step. Be sure to tap the ball far enough ahead so that you don't have to slow down for the next tap. Don't tap the ball so far ahead that you lose control of it or give a defensive player a chance to steal it.

Dribbling to the Right and Left

If you want the ball to go to the left, use the inside of your right foot or the outside of your left foot to tap the ball to the left. To move the ball to the right, use the inside of your left foot or the outside of your right foot to tap the ball to the right. Which foot you use depends on which foot you are standing on when you need to tap the ball. If your weight is on your right foot, then use your left foot to tap the ball.

Keeping the Ball Close

To move the ball just a little bit and still keep it very close to you, use the sole of your foot to drag the ball. Step lightly on the top of the ball and drag your foot to the side, bringing the ball along. You can also use this move to drag the ball backward.

Practice, Practice, Practice

Practice dribbling forward, backward, and to the sides. Practice using all the parts of your feet to control the ball. Pretend that trees, lawn chairs, and bushes are defensive players, and try to weave around them while dribbling. The more you practice your dribbling skills, the better soccer player you'll become.

Dribbling in a Game

Soccer isn't like basketball, where one player slowly jogs, dribbling the ball, waiting to run a play. In soccer, everyone is involved, and the flow of the game goes something like this: One player takes three dribbles, then passes the ball to a teammate, who takes six dribbles and passes to another teammate, who takes four dribbles and passes the ball, and so on. During a game, the ball can be dribbled in any direction in order to get it away from defensive players or to move it toward an open area of the field. It's very important to know when to dribble and when not to.

When to Dribble

You should dribble:

- When you have a small area to cross and no defensive players are challenging you. There's no point in risking a pass if the defense is letting you move freely.

3-3: There are times when you should dribble and times to get rid of the ball. Open space in front of you down the sideline is a good time to carry the ball.

- On a *breakaway* down the sideline (Figure 3-3). Breakaway means that you've gotten away from the opponents and are running alone, or there's just one opponent to beat. Often you'll be able to sprint and dribble a good distance before passing the ball to a teammate who is waiting by the goal.

- When you need time to organize an attack on the goal.

When Not to Dribble

Don't dribble:

- If a defensive player challenges you. It's safer to pass the ball to a teammate.

- When a teammate is open for a pass. Dribbling isn't as fast as passing. If a teammate opens up, it's better to send the ball speeding down the field toward him than to try to dribble it there yourself.

- In your own goal area.

Keep Control While Dribbling

In dribbling, the ball should be kept close enough to your feet, so that you can always reach it in one step. That means that if you're sprinting (running fast), it can be a little farther out in front than if you're just jogging. Many players think that if they kick the ball way out in front of them while sprinting they can run faster and get to the goal sooner, but it doesn't do any good to get to the goal if they lose the ball on the way. A ball farther than one step away from you is no longer in your control, and any good defensive player can move in and snatch it away.

Protecting the Ball from the Defense

Sometimes you have to use your ball handling (dribbling) skills to protect the ball from a defensive player. This is a completely different type of dribbling. You'll be moving forward, backward, and side to side, using the tops of your feet, the bottoms of your feet, the toes, the heels, and the sides of your feet. Keep your body between the ball and your opponent. This may mean backing up, until you can get by him (Figure 3-4).

Cuts and Fakes

If the defensive player isn't right on top of you, you can use sharp *cuts* (changes in direction) and *fakes* (acting like you're going to do one thing, then doing another) to get away from him (Figure 3-5). Cuts have to be fast, and fakes have to look real. A lazy fake isn't going to fool anyone. Here are a few moves you can use to get by a defender:

3-4: Use your body to shield the ball from the defender. If he can't get at the ball, he can't take it away. 3-5: Faking in one direction and cutting back to the other is a good way to get past a defender. 3-6: Fancy footwork should only be used in a game by advanced and more experienced players. Here the player has stepped over the ball with his right leg, planted with his left, and is now ready to continue in the opposite direction. The defender is fooled, and has little chance of recovering.

Cut Back

If the defensive player is coming at you fast, on an angle, cut toward him, while keeping the ball away from his feet. Since he's moving fast, he won't be able to stop quickly and you can slide right by him (Figure 3-6). It will be hard to do this at first, because your instinct will be to move away from him. But if you move away from him, he can stay right on top of you, so force yourself to cut toward him.

Stutter Step

When you're sprinting down the sideline and want to pass to a teammate in the middle of the field, and a defensive player is right next to you, try the *stutter step*. First get your speed up, then stop. As soon as you stop, start going again. This should put you one step ahead of your opponent and allow you to pass the ball to the center of the field.

Q **A** *Who has been the greatest influence on your soccer career?*

My father, Bill, and the rest of my family really helped me while I was growing up. They made it possible for me to receive a scholarship to a great soccer school like Rutgers University (in New Jersey).

Professionally, I think the biggest influence came from coach Gary Henley, who is currently coach of the Buffalo Blizzard professional soccer team. He gave me a lot of guidance and direction when I came out of college and showed me how to be a professional.

Q **A** *What is the most important thing a young person can do to become a good soccer player.?*

Never give up and keep training. Always try to learn from other people. You also have to make sure you work hard in school. If you don't, you won't be able to achieve your goals.

Q **A** *Describe the feeling of playing soccer to represent your country?*

It's definitely a privilege and an incredible experience. As you travel, you know that there are only a handful of players chosen to represent your country. You always dream of it as a youngster, and when it actually happens, it makes all the hard work and time worth it.

Q **A** *What was the most satisfying moment in your soccer career?*

Being able to play in the Major League Soccer championship game for the Rochester Rhinos this summer was great. Also, helping Mercer County Community College to a national championship was unforgettable for me. I played in a lot of championship games in my career, but that's the only time my team won. The feeling of being a part of a winning team is very special.

Q **A** *What advice would you give youngsters hoping to excel in soccer?*

Soccer is a great game, but make sure you stay in school and are a well-rounded person. Sports are great, but education is the key to being successful in life. A young person who combines success with hard work in the classroom will have every chance for success in life.

If you're sprinting down the sideline and want to dribble to the center of the field, use a slightly different stutter step. As soon as you stop, drag the ball backward slightly and make a quick, sharp cut to the center of the field (Figure 3-7).

Rock and Roll

This is a good fake to use when you're moving backward to keep your body between the ball and a defensive player and the defensive player is between you and the goal. When you *rock and roll*, you do a lot of body moves, so keep your knees bent and your body low so you won't get off balance. Back right into your defender while looking over one shoulder. Then rock your body in the direction you're looking, just like you are going to break (move) that way. As soon as the defender commits (starts to move) in that direction, drag the ball backward in the opposite direction with the bottom of your foot, roll your body away from him, and head down the field.

Once you've used the rock and roll a few times in a game, your defensive player will be expecting you to do it again. You can catch him off guard by doing a double fake. Rock one way, start to roll the other way, and then roll back the first way.

Fancy Footwork

When there's a defensive player right on top of you, you need to use all your ball handling skills and do some *fancy footwork*. Drag the ball one way, nudge it another way, step over it sideways, then tap it back the other way with the outside of the foot. You can step over the ball and push it behind that leg with the inside of the other foot. Lean one way and cut the other. Fake with your head and your body. The style of your fancy footwork depends on you but you must keep contact with the ball at all times so you won't lose control of it.

Slalom Drill

Set up obstacles (use chairs, cones, flags, other players, caps, or even sweatshirts) in a line, about four or five steps apart. Dribble in and out of the obstacles as fast as you can without losing the ball. If you use other players as your obstacles, they can try to get the ball from you as you dribble around them, and you will have to protect the ball like you would in a game. When you're done dribbling through the obstacle course, you can become one of the obstacles and let another player take a turn at dribbling.

Relay Races

In a relay race, members of a team (two to four players) take turns dribbling the ball down the field while racing against another team. The first person on each team starts at one endline and dribbles the ball part way down the field. The second person on the team (who's been waiting there) takes over dribbling until they get farther down the field, where the third person on the team takes over, and so on. The first team to dribble the ball to the other endline is the winner of the relay race.

Use relay races to practice one dribbling skill. If you want to practice using the outside of your foot to dribble, set up a race where that's the only kind of dribbling allowed. Then run another relay race where the ball must be dragged with the sole of the foot. Use relay races to practice moving the ball with the left or right foot only.

3-7: Dribbling is useful, but always know when to give the ball up. If you carry too long, eventually a defender will catch up and gain possession of the ball.

Make It Up, Play It Out

Here's two games that are fun ways to practice your dribbling skills.

Duck

You need eight or more players, a soccer ball for every player, and a playing area. One player is the duck. He dribbles around the outside of the rest of the players who are standing in a circle, and stops between two players. These two players take off dribbling around the circle in opposite directions. The duck takes one of the player's spots and the person who dribbled around the circle the fastest, takes the other empty spot. The slower dribbler gets a D and he becomes the duck. The game continues and the slowest person always gets a letter, first a D, then a U, then a C, then a K. When someone has spelled D-U-C-K, he is out of the game. The winner is the last one left in the game.

Through the Legs

You need four players, a soccer ball, a timer, and a playing area. There are two people on each team. One player from each team makes a "goal" by spreading his legs apart. The two "goals" stand about 30 feet apart. The other two players battle it out in between the goals.

A goal is scored when the ball goes through the legs of the opponent's goal, either forward or backward. The players who act as the goals may not move their legs to block the ball.

One of the goals should be holding the timer. After two minutes, the two players become the goals and the two goals become the players. The team with the most goals is the winner.

Keep Focused

1. Dribbling is used to move the ball down the field and to move it around a defensive player.
2. Use all parts of your foot to dribble.
3. Keep your head up.
4. Control is important, so keep the ball no farther than a step away from you.
5. Dribbling is not as fast as passing the ball.
6. Use fakes and cuts to fool the defender.
7. Practice dribbling whenever you can, and it will make you a better soccer player.

Passing

P assing means transferring (moving) the ball from one player to another. A soccer field is big, and good passing is the only way to get the ball from one end to the other without the other team stealing the ball. A team that masters passing will have control of the playing field.

Basic Passes

Passes can be short or long. They can be on the ground or through the air. Here's some basic passes:

The Inside-of-the-Foot Pass

The *inside-of-the-foot pass* is the most basic pass (Figure 4-1). It is used for short distances. Take a step or a hop forward with your non-kicking foot and *plant* (put your weight on) it about three or four inches on the outside of the ball. The toes of your planted foot should be pointing in the direction you want the ball to go. Lean forward over your planted foot so that your body is almost directly over the ball. Keep your eye on the ball as you move your kicking foot back and off the ground. Keep the inside of your kicking foot lined up with the ball and keep your ankle stiff. The motion for this

4-1: Passing the ball with the inside of the foot is for short, quick passes. The backswing is minimal to ensure accuracy.

4-2: Delivering the ball with the instep of the foot is primarily used for long passes. The backswing is greater to generate more power.

kick comes from your hip. Swing your whole kicking leg forward from your hip, and kick through the center of the ball with enough force to send it to your teammate. After you kick the ball, make sure you *follow through* (let your leg continue in the direction of the pass). The follow-through will help your kick be more accurate (go where you aim it).

The Instep Pass

The inside of the foot can give you accuracy when passing, but it doesn't give your kick much power. To put power into your kick, you need to use the *instep*, which is the top part of your foot (the part that is covered by your shoelaces) (Figure 4-2). The instep kick is used more than any other kick in soccer. It is especially good when you need to send the ball over a long distance, but it can be used for shorter distances, too.

Plant one foot near the outside of the ball. Point your planted foot in the direction you want the ball to go. Keep your eye on the ball as you move your kicking foot back and off the ground (Figure 4-3). Keep the toes of your kicking foot pointed straight down. Swing the kicking leg forward, keeping your ankle stiff. Strike the ball in the center with the top of your instep, *not your toes*. Snap your knee (move your lower leg forward) at the moment of impact (contact). Use enough force to send the ball to your teammate.

Like the inside-of-the-foot kick, the instep kick gets much of its power from the hip, but it also gets power from the snap of the knee at the moment of impact. At the end of the kick, your leg and foot should be straight. Some players make the mistake of kicking the ball, then pulling their leg back as if the ball were

4-3: This player is getting ready to deliver an instep pass. You can tell he's about use his instep because his kicking toe is pointed down, and he's using a big backswing.

4-4: When kicking the ball long, such as a goal kick, your best method is to lift the ball into the air. By doing so, you avoid having an opponent intercept a pass before it reaches your target.

hot. This is a mistake. You need to follow through with the bottom half of your leg.

To kick the ball in a straight line, you need to strike it in the very center. If you strike the ball to the right or left of its center, you will put *spin* on the ball. Spin means that the ball turns while it's traveling. There are times when you want the ball to curve in or out, allowing you to send it around a defensive player. Practice kicking to the right and left of the center of the ball, putting spin on it, so you learn how to send the ball on a curving path.

The Lofted Pass

Lofting means passing the ball through the air. A lofted pass is harder for your teammate to get under control, but there are times you want to use this pass. For example, if you see your teammate flying down the sideline, wide open for a pass, and there are defensive players between you and him. If you pass the ball along the ground, it might be *intercepted* (taken) by an opponent. You can send a lofted pass over the heads of the defensive players so it lands just in front of your running teammate.

To send a lofted pass, the ball needs to be farther out in front of you (about 18 inches) than with the instep pass. Hop off your kicking foot and plant your non-kicking foot. The hop needs to be a big one in order to give your body the power to kick hard. When you plant your foot, it should be about eight to 12 inches from the ball. Your planted foot should be behind and off to the side of the ball. Keep your weight on the heel of your planted foot (Figure 4-4). This will force you to lean backward when you

4-5, 4-6: When chipping the ball, you need to get the ball elevated quickly. Plant your foot slightly further behind the ball than you normally would. Lean back with your body, and kick the ball near the front of your laces. This a finesse pass that requires very little power behind it.

kick, instead of forward, over the ball. Move your kicking foot back and off the ground. Keep your toes pointed straight down. Use your instep to strike the ball in the center, on the bottom side. This will send the ball into the air.

If you make the kick correctly, your planting foot is behind you, your body is leaning back, and your knee is behind the ball. This position helps you to hit the underside of the ball with your instep.

Because the ball is so far in front of you before you take your kick, you won't be able to protect it at that time. Don't use a lofted pass if a defensive player is right on top of you.

The Chip

The *chip* is a very short pass through the air. Plant your foot about three or four inches on the outside of the ball (Figure 4-5). The toes of your planted foot should be pointing in the direction you want the ball to go. Lean forward over your planted foot so that your body is almost directly over the ball. Strike the ball as far underneath as possible with the instep of your kicking foot (Figure 4-6). This gives the ball its loft. Because you are so close to the ball, striking it can be difficult. The chip does not have as much power as a lofted pass. The ball should pop up into the air about 10 or 15 feet.

The Volley

A *volley* is when the ball is passed through the air to you and you send it away without the ball ever touching the ground. As the ball flies to you, use the instep of your foot to strike the ball while it is still in the air (Figure 4-7). The ball must come directly off your instep, not your toes (which will affect your aim), or the side of your foot (which will cause you to lose power).

The volley is most often used to shoot the ball at the goal, but it can be used for a pass, too.

The Drop Kick

The *drop kick* is also called the *half volley*. It's almost the same move as the volley, but the ball bounces once before you send it on to your teammate. Don't try the drop kick until you are good at the volley.

On the drop kick, you need to concentrate on your timing. Let the ball hit the ground and in the split second that it starts to *rebound* (bounce back up), kick it with your instep as you would a volley. The nice thing about this kick is that you won't catch your toes on the ground, like you sometimes do with other instep kicks. The problem with the drop kick is, if your timing is off, you'll hit the ball with your shin. With lots of practice, you'll learn perfect timing.

The Outside-of-the-Foot Pass

Sometimes, when there's an unguarded teammate close to you, you can nudge (gently push) the ball to him. You can do this easily with the inside of your foot, but you should learn how to do it with the outside of your foot, too. Make contact with the ball with the outside of your foot and give a quick flick (bend) of your ankle to send the ball to your teammate. This pass doesn't have much power, but it does allow you to keep your body between the ball and the defensive player and still make a pass.

The One-Touch Pass

Most of the time you want to bring the ball under control before you pass it, but sometimes there isn't enough time to do this. That's when you use a *one-touch pass*. The ball comes toward you, and you touch it once, sending it in another direction without bringing it under control first. Use the one-touch pass:

1. When a defensive player is all over you and you may lose the ball if you try to bring it under control.

2. When a teammate is making a great run and you want to get the ball to him as quickly as possible.

4-7: When striking a volley, try to use the instep. Keep your eye on the soccer ball all the way into your foot to ensure solid contact.

The one-touch pass isn't easy. Some players just boot the ball as hard as they can. This won't be a controlled pass and the other team may intercept the ball. To have control of a one-touch pass, kick the ball near the top. This will take some of the power away from the ball and allow you to direct it to your teammate.

Control When Passing

Many beginning players think that power is what matters most when passing. You'll see them kicking the ball with the end of their shoes (called a toe kick). They can send the ball far, but they have no idea where it's going. That's no way to play soccer. You must always know who is receiving the ball, how to place the ball, and how to pass it in order for that teammate to get it.

The Wall Drill

The wall drill is a great way to practice controlling your kicks. Kick the ball into a wall so that it will bounce back toward you. When it bounces back, kick it at the wall. Practice the way you would be playing in a game, by making passes on the run, and by using all the different kinds of passes.

4-8: Passing the ball upfield is much faster than dribbling. Always keep your head up and look for open teammates to move the ball up the field quickly.

Beyond Control

Once you learn how to control your passes, here are several things you can do to make your controlled passes better:

1. **Look at the ball as you make contact.** Perfect passing skills don't mean much if you miss the ball.

2. **Don't let the defense know where you will be sending the pass.** Try not to look at the player you're passing to. If you fool the defense, you have a much better chance of making a successful pass.

3. **You don't always have to move the ball forward.** If your teammates ahead of you are all guarded by defenders, don't risk losing the ball just to move it closer to the goal. By passing to a teammate on the side of you, or even behind you, the guarded teammates have a chance to get free while your team still has control of the ball.

4. **Lead your teammate with the ball.** You always want to send the ball slightly out in front of where your teammate is so he can reach the ball without breaking his stride.

The Weave Drill

The weave is a passing drill for three players that helps you learn how to lead your teammate when passing to him. Divide the field into three lanes. Players stand on the endline, one at the beginning of each lane. The player in the center lane has the ball. He takes a dribble or two, then passes the ball either left or right, sending it out in front of his running teammate. As soon as the ball leaves his foot, he chases after the ball and runs behind his teammate. The teammate who has received the pass moves to the center lane, and passes the ball to the third player. Again, the player passing the ball follows the ball and runs behind the receiver, who moves to the center lane. The drill ends when one player takes a shot on the goal.

Make It Up, Play It Out

Six in a Row

You need six players, a soccer ball, and a field. The object of the game is for one team to make six passes in a row without the other team touching the ball. This is hard to do because the other team is allowed to try to intercept the passes. Every time a team gets six passes in a row, they get one point. If it's too hard to get six passes in a row, you can change it to three or four passes. The team with the most points, wins the game.

Hot Potato

You need four or more players, a soccer ball, a timer with a buzzer, and a playing area. Players form a circle, standing about every three feet apart, and facing the center of the circle. Set the timer for 45 seconds and pass the ball to one another as fast as possible. The player who touched the ball last when the buzzer goes off is out. The last player remaining is the winner.

Set the timer for a different number of seconds on each turn. Instead of eliminating a player on the first buzzer, you can have a player spell P-O-T-A-T-O (or a shorter

4-9: Passing can be done out of the air also. When preparing for a headball, know where your teammates are and head the ball in their direction.

word) before he is out. Give a player a P the first time he is stuck with the ball, an O the second time, and so on.

Dodge Ball

You need 10 or more players, one or more soccer balls, a timer, and a playing area. Players are divided into two teams. One team forms a large circle, and the other team stands at different places inside the circle. The team that forms the circle kicks one or more soccer balls, trying to hit the players inside the circle. When a player gets hit, he is out and must leave the circle.

Time how long it takes for the outside team to get all the inside players out. Then the two teams change places and play begins again. The winner is the team that gets all the inside players out in the shortest time.

You can also play this game by having the teams take three-minute turns. The winner is the team that knocks out the most players in three minutes.

Progressive Dodge Ball

You need 10 or more players, a soccer ball for every player, markers such as caps, cones or flags, and a playing area. Mark off a large circle. All players stay inside the circle. At the beginning of the game, only one player has a ball. He tries to hit any of the other players by kicking the ball at them. Once any player gets hit, he gets a ball and becomes an attacker. The last player left is the winner.

1. Passing is the most important soccer skill.
2. Passing options include the inside-of-the-foot-pass, the instep pass, the lofted pass, the chip, the volley, the drop kick, the outside-of-the-foot-pass, and the one-touch pass.
3. Look at the ball when you kick it.
4. Make your passes sharp and snappy.
5. Lead your teammate with the ball.
6. Don't force the pass if your teammate isn't open.
7. Make sure that your passes are controlled.
8. Practice the way you play in a game.

CHAPTER 5

Receiving the Ball

Imagine a soccer team where one player has the ball and the rest of the players just stand around and watch him. Boring, huh? It would be an easy team to play against because there wouldn't be any passing!

Now imagine a team where the players are always on the run. The ball is moving quickly around the field, the defensive team is thrown off guard, and a beautiful, clear shot opens up. That's the game of soccer!

Passing takes two players, a passer and a receiver. If the receiver isn't in a good position to get the pass, even the best passer will have trouble sending the ball to him.

Moving to Receive the Ball

When one of your teammates has the ball, you want to move to a position on the field where you might be able to receive a pass. Here are five ways that you can get in a good position:

1. **Keep moving.** Make sharp cuts. It's hard for the defense to stay with you if you keep moving.

5-1: Don't bunch up with your teammates. Running in close to your teammate draws in another defender and clogs up passing lanes. Spread out and use the field.

2. **Go to the open spaces.** This often means moving out to the sidelines or sprinting down the field. Keep away from the defense as much as possible.

3. **Don't bunch** (crowd your teammates). As much as you want to stay away from the defense, you also want to stay away from your teammates (Figure 5-1). If your team is spread out on the field, the passer has more choices of teammates to pass to.

4. **Stay open.** Even though you want to move into an empty area of the field, it won't help the passer if there are defensive players between you and him.

5. **Know the passer's skills.** Sprinting down the sideline can be a great breakaway move, but if your passer isn't able to loft the ball to you, it's useless. Know which passes your teammates are good at and adjust yourself to their abilities.

In addition to the five tips listed above, there are special pass plays that you can use to make more chances for passing.

Square

The *square* is a pass that goes directly out to the side. Some receivers yell "square right" or "square left," but usually the passer will be able to see which side of the field the receiver is running to. The receiver should call out "square" as he's approaching the spot where he's going to receive the pass. If the receiver yells out "square" after he's already there, the defense can get to him while he waits for the ball.

Wing

The *wing* pass is a sideline pass. Cut to the edge of the field and sprint toward the goal, yelling "wing." Usually the passer will have to send a lofted kick in your direction to get the ball over the top of the defense.

Wall

The *wall* pass is also known as the *give and go* or the *one-two* pass (Figures 5-2 through 5-4). The term, "wall pass," probably comes from indoor soccer, where a passer bounces the ball off a wall, then sprints to catch it, in order to get the ball around a defensive player.

In outdoor soccer, the passer calls out "wall," sends the ball to you, then sprints beyond the defensive player. When you receive a wall pass, let the ball bounce off you, around the

5-2 through 5-4: A wall pass is one of the best ways to move the ball up the field. Send a pass on the ground to your teammate and race forward. Your teammate should kick the ball "first-time" and hit you with a lead pass.

defensive player, and toward the sprinting passer, who gets the ball back. When you're the wall, you can help a bit by nudging the ball in the right direction.

Overlap

When your team has the ball, some of your players are moving to attack your opponent's goal and they are able to pass and receive passes. Other team members will be hanging back to defend your goal in case the other team gets the ball. These team members on defense usually don't receive passes because they aren't moving toward the opponent's goal. (There's more about player positions on the field in Chapter 10 on Strategy.) In the *overlap* pass (as shown in the diagram), if you're playing defense for your team, you can suddenly become one of your team's attackers by sprinting down the sideline from behind the other players, yelling, "overlap." You should only do this if there is an open spot for you to run to.

With the overlap pass, you give your team's passer an extra person that he can pass to—you. This can mess up the other team's defense and maybe make some openings for your teammates.

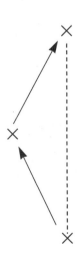

Back

A *back* pass is another way to keep the ball away from the defense. The passer steps over the ball, then uses his heel to kick it backward to you. Because the defense is moving forward, and the ball has been passed backward, you should be in the clear. This is a good time for you to send the ball to a teammate on the other side of the field where it is less crowded.

Talking to Your Team on the Field

Be sure to call out the names of the different plays correctly so that your teammates understand the play. Just calling a teammate's name, "Chris!" or yelling "Chris, I'm free!" doesn't give Chris as much information as shouting, "back!" Different teams use different words to describe pass moves. For example, some teams use the words, "give and go," for the wall pass, and other teams just use the word, "wall." Everyone on your team should use the same words.

Besides calling out pass moves, tell your passer when someone is coming up on him. Tell him when he has time to settle the ball and get control, and when he has to get rid of the ball quickly. He has to keep his eyes on the ball, so help him out by telling him what's happening on the rest of the field.

Never call out a pass play if you're not free to receive the ball. If the passer hears you call, "square," he's going to assume that he's clear to pass in that direction.

Trapping the Ball with Your Feet

Moving into the right position is only one skill you need to be a good receiver. You also need to know how to catch the ball with your feet. Most people aren't used to catching a ball with their feet. Toes, especially those covered by shoes, can't grip like fingers can. Since you can't actually grab the ball with your feet, you must learn to *trap* it (stop it and bring it under control).

Trapping Balls on the Ground

You can use the inside of your foot to stop balls that come to you on the ground. Your toes should be up and your ankle should be stiff. Place the inside of your foot slightly above the ball's middle (Figure 5-5). If you contact the ball lower down, it will bounce out of control. If you contact the ball higher up, it might roll right under your foot.

Another way to trap a ball on the ground is to step on it as it gets to you and trap it between your foot and the ground. (Never try to trap a ball this way when it's in the air. If your timing is off, you'll miss or step on the ball wrong and turn your ankle.)

Trapping Balls Coming Out of the Air

If the ball is coming out of the air toward the ground, stick your foot out in front of the ball, point your toes, contact the ball with the front end of your foot, and let the ball push your foot back a little bit. Then pull your foot away and the ball should drop right in front of you (Figure 5-6). If you don't let the ball push your foot back a little, the ball will bounce off your foot in the direction it came from instead of landing nicely at your feet.

5-5: Trap the ball with the inside of your foot slightly above the ball's middle. To keep the ball under control, "give" with it as you make your trap. The foot should be held soft, not stiff.

Middle Man Passing Drill

Three players line up about 10 to 15 feet apart from one another. Each of the end players has a ball. The middle player is the receiver. One end player passes the ball on the ground to the receiver. He traps it, passes it back, and quickly turns toward the other end player, who has already sent him a pass. The receiver traps the ball, passes it

5-6, 5-7: There are two methods of trapping the ball out of the air with your foot. The first is to use the side of the foot as shown in Figure 5-6. Use this when the ball is slightly off the ground. When the ball is a little higher (just below the knee cap), use the laces (5-7). Pull your foot away as you catch the ball and allow it to drop to the ground.

back, and turns to the other end player, who has already sent him another pass. After two minutes, players change positions.

After all three players have taken a turn receiving the ball on the ground, repeat the drill, using lofted passes that come out of the air toward the ground.

5-8: The thigh trap takes quick reactions and a soft touch. Catch the ball with your thigh and gain control of it with your feet.

5-9: The chest trap is valuable when you have time to control the ball. Arch your back as the ball hits your chest and then get it under control with your feet.

Trapping the Ball with Your Body

A third receiving skill you need to learn is using your body to trap the ball.

Trapping Balls Coming Straight through the Air

Sometimes the ball is coming straight through the air instead of heading toward the ground. In this case, you won't be able to use your foot to stop the ball, so you have to use another part of your body, such as your inner thigh (Figure 5-8), your chest, or another part of your trunk.

The chest is probably the most popular part of the body to use for trapping by boys (Figure 5-9), while the rest of the trunk or the inner thigh is more popular to use for trapping by girls. Either way, you want to let your body move backward a bit with the ball so the ball won't bounce off you in another direction when it hits you. This is very hard to do with your whole body, so expect the ball to bounce off you sometimes when it hits you. To make up for this bounce, try to run right through the ball after you trap it, and push the ball in the direction that you are going.

Through-the-Air Passing Drill

In this drill, two players face each other, one standing on the endline of the soccer field and the other on the field, about five yards away. The player on the endline has the ball. The receiver runs backward while the other player runs forward and uses his hands to toss the ball through the air at the receiver. No matter where the ball is tossed, the receiver must trap it with his body, drop it to his feet, and pass it back to the other player.

Receiving the One-Touch Pass

When the ball is passed to you, and the other team's defense is all over you, you don't have time to trap the ball and get it under control before passing it on to another teammate. In this case, don't try to trap the ball. Use *one touch* to send it on to a teammate who is open.

Make It Up, Play It Out

Two games that will help you develop your receiving skills are Corners and Wallball.

Corners

You need four players, a soccer ball, a square playing area, and markers, such as hats, cones, or flags. Place a marker on each corner of the playing area. Three of the players stand in different corners of the square. The corner players keep passing the ball to each other, but they may only pass the ball along the lines of the square, never through the middle. When a corner player has the ball, he should have a choice of passing the ball to either of the other two passers, so the other two corner players may have to change corners quickly in order to fill an empty corner next to the passer (the corner opposite the passer should always be empty).

The fourth player tries to steal the ball as it is passed from corner to corner. If he steals the ball, he trades places with the passer who passed the ball, and the game continues.

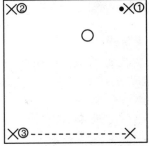

When player 1 has possession of the ball, player 3 should run over to the bottom right corner to give player 1 another clear passing lane.

Wallball

You need two players, a soccer ball, and a wall. One player kicks the ball through the air against the wall. The other player has to trap the ball, then kick the ball at the wall for the first player to trap. When a player misses trapping the ball or lets it touch the ground before trapping it, the other player gets a point. The first player to get 15 points is the winner.

Keep Focused

1. Receivers must keep in motion and move to the open spaces.
2. Don't bunch with other members of your team; try to spread out your team's offense.
3. Make sure that there are no defensive players between you and the passer.
4. Talk to your teammates by calling out pass plays or warning them when they need to get rid of the ball quickly.
5. When trapping passes coming out of the air toward the ground, use your foot to take the speed off the ball.
6. When the ball is coming to you, and you need to send it quickly in another direction, use a one-touch pass.

6

Heading

In a soccer game, you use your head for more than thinking. If the ball is coming toward you through the air, your head is the first weapon you have to control the flight (direction) of the ball. *Heading* (hitting the ball with your head) is a very important soccer skill.

Getting Hurt

When you head the ball correctly, you use only your forehead (the area between your eyebrows and your hairline) to strike the ball. When you're first learning heading, it can be painful, because you'll probably make a lot of mistakes. The most painful mistake is hitting the ball with your face. To make these "face balls," less painful, practice with a beach ball, or let some of the air out of your soccer ball to make it soft. As your heading skills improve, you can switch to a regular soccer ball.

Don't let your fear of getting hurt keep you from learning heading. Once you learn the correct way to head the ball, it won't hurt. A player who won't head the ball because he's afraid, or who only makes a half-hearted try, won't be a great soccer player.

Heading Basics

The following basic steps will teach you how to head the ball correctly.

Get into Position

Getting into the *right position* for heading is very important. If you're even a couple of inches off, you'll make a mistake. When you see the ball coming toward you through the air, move so the ball will land right in the center of your forehead. The most common mistake young players make when getting into position is to move too far forward and the ball skims off their hair.

Watch the Ball

You must *watch the ball* all the way to your forehead in order to prevent a painful hit on the top of your head or on your nose. Always head the ball with your eyes open.

6-1, 6-2: To get power behind your headball, you need to use your entire upper body. Use your legs as a firm base beneath, and lean back at the mid-section (6-1). As the ball gets to you, snap your head and neck forward, using your forehead to strike the ball.

Keep Your Upper Body Stiff, Snap from Your Waist

Some young players think that the head has to *snap* (jerk) forward on impact (contact) with the ball in order to put force behind the ball. This isn't true. When you hit the ball with your head, it's very important to keep your neck and your whole upper body very *stiff*. To snap the ball correctly, lean backward as it comes to you, then snap forward *from your waist* on impact. The ball shouldn't hit you—you should hit the ball. Keep your feet wide apart and your knees bent to help you stay balanced during the snap (Figures 6-1 and 6-2).

There are two good reasons for keeping your upper body stiff and making the snap with your waist. The first is to avoid whiplash (injury to your neck from having it suddenly snapped forward or backward). The second reason is to give the ball some power. If your neck is loose when you head the ball, the ball will push your head back. But if your neck is stiff, the energy from the ball will go into the bounce off your head.

Control the Hit

You can *control* where the ball goes by controlling what part of the ball you contact. If you want the ball to go on a sharp angle toward the ground, hit it on its top half. If you want to send the ball on a straight line, hit it close to its center. Never hit the ball below its center or it will pop up in the air and lose much of its power.

Keep Your Hands and Arms Away from the Ball

Don't use your *hands and arms* to protect your head from the ball. If you use your hands on the ball during a game, it's a foul, and the other team will get a direct free kick on your goal.

Head Toss Drill

Two players stand five to seven yards apart. One player is the server (thrower) and the other player is the header. The server throws (underhand throwing is best) the ball to the header who heads the ball back to the server. After a few serves, the ball is thrown a little higher and the header jumps for it. After a few jumps, the players run down the field while the ball is served and headed. After 10 serves, the server becomes the header, the header becomes the server, and the drill is repeated (Figures 6-3 and 6-4).

Q **A** *When did you first become interested in soccer?*

I first started playing when I was 12. There was a league in my hometown. They didn't really have club ball then, so I just joined for something to do. I saw it as a chance to meet other kids.

Q **A** *What is the most important thing a young person can do to become a good soccer player?*

First and foremost, you have to do it because it's fun. I loved every minute that I played. I think that's true of all my teammates. We played because we couldn't imagine doing anything else.

Q **A** *What can you gain as a person from playing soccer?*

I think you realize that there's something special about being part of a team. You learn quickly that your actions have an effect on all your teammates. If you don't feel like training, or running, you have to stop and think that you are letting down your teammates and that's just not fair.

Q **A** *Is there more to sports than just winning and losing?*

I think sports are a method of expressing yourself. I think you can discover an interesting side of yourself by playing sports. You can almost be an entirely different person out on the field.

Soccer also helped me develop tremendous discipline. You really learn how to manage your time when you're training, playing and taking care of schoolwork.

Q **A** *What was it like to win the Olympic gold medal in Atlanta?*

When they put the Olympic medal around your neck, it's sort of hard to believe. I had thought a lot about winning a gold medal, but when I did it was the most amazing moment of my life. I'd worked all my life for that moment and it seemed like time stood still. And to hear 76,000 fans singing their anthem, that's something I'll never forget.

6-3, 6-4: Stand about 15 to 20 feet apart from your teammate. Head the ball back and forth without allowing the ball to hit the ground. This will improve your accuracy on headballs.

Heading to the Side

Once you've learned to hit the ball square in the center of your forehead, it's time to learn how to use the edges of your forehead to send the ball to the side. Many times during a game the ball will be coming to you on an angle from the sideline and you want to head it into the goal. Other times the ball will be coming to you straight and you want to head it to an open teammate who is to your left or right.

When the ball is heading toward you, lean your body to the side instead of backward. When you snap from your waist, make the snap to one side instead of forward. This means that you will hit the ball with one side of your forehead instead of the middle, and the ball will go to the side. Make sure you hit the ball with the side of your forehead, not your ear (Figures 6-5 through 6-7).

Heading Backward

If you want to send the ball backward and you have a defender right behind you, it's hard to get the ball under control in front of you and then move the ball around him. In this case, *heading the ball backward*, over his head is a good move. A backward head ball looks the same as a forward head ball until the moment of contact. Then, instead of snapping the body forward, flick (jerk)

6-5 through 6-7: To head the ball to either side, use the side of your head in which direction you want the ball to go. When heading the ball to the left, move your head to the right of the ball as it comes to you. Watch the ball come in and snap your head to the left to strike the ball. Keep your eyes open (6-6). Make sure you follow through to maximize power on your headball (6-7).

just your head backward, contacting the ball on its lower half. You're not really heading the ball; you're just keeping it in the air longer.

Another reason for using this backward head flick is to keep up the ball's momentum (force). If you see a teammate making a great run, flick the ball backward to him with your head instead of taking the time to get the ball under control first.

Getting Up for Headballs

A lot of loose balls are won and lost out of the air. It's important that a player (offensive or defensive) knows how to get up off his feet and win a headball. Once you recognize that you're going to have to leave your feet to get your head on the ball, here's what you should concentrate on:

- **Know your target before you leave the ground.** Once you're in the air, your eyes should be focused on the ball, and not what's going on around you.

- **Time your jump with the arrival of the ball.** You should be at the height of your leap as the ball reaches you. If you're early or late it will have an effect on the strength and accuracy of your headball.

6-8: When going up in the air for a headball, make sure you keep your hands down by your side. If they're up and make contact with your opponent, a foul will often be called.

- **Go straight up and keep your hands down.** If you jump or lean into an opponent when going up for a headball, you may be called for a foul. It's also very important to keep your hands down at your sides (Figure 6-8).

- **Use your upper body.** You can't get any power from your legs when you're already in the air, so the power has to come from the upper-half of your body. You need to get good snap from your neck and torso.

Jumping Header Drill

Two players stand about two feet apart. One player holds the ball firmly in his hands up above his head and out away from his body. The other player stands stationary, takes one step, and leaps up to head the ball. Make sure you practice snapping your head forward and keep you eyes open. Head the ball ten times in a row without a break and then switch with your partner.

Get in Shape

You need strong muscles to make good head shots. When you are heading, the power comes from your stomach and back muscles. The Crunch Drill, Leg Push Drill, and Rocker Drill in Chapter 2 are good exercises for building this strength. To strengthen your neck, use the Neck Muscles Drill (also in Chapter 2).

Make It Up, Play It Out

Here's a game that will help you and your teammates practice heading skills.

Heading Tennis

You need four or more players, a soccer ball, and a tennis court or playing area with a net that is four to six feet high (the net can be a badminton net, or just a piece of string held up by two posts). Each team takes one side of the net. One player serves (throws) the ball over the net to the other team.

The members of the other team must use their heads to return the ball over the net. The ball can bounce once before it is headed and it may be headed by more than one team member before being returned over the net. The serving team must head the ball back over the net. When a team fails to head the ball back over the net, the other team gets one point. After each point, the ball is served by the team that made the point. The team with the most points at the end of the game is the winner.

6-9: Headballs are a great way to score goals. The goalkeeper has very little time to react because the offensive player is simply re-directing the cross.

Keep Focused

1. When you first practice heading, use a soft ball.
2. Make sure you're in a good position when the ball is coming toward you.
3. Keep your neck stiff, and snap forward from your waist when heading the ball.
4. Keep your eyes open and watch the ball while heading.
5. Use your forehead to make contact with the upper half of the ball.
6. Heading to the side, heading backward, and jumping headers are other ways to use your head in the game.
7. You need strong muscles to make good head shots.

CHAPTER 7

Shooting

One player crosses the ball in front of the goal. His teammate rushes in to trap the pass. He brings the ball under control but the defense is all over him. He takes a quick dribble and sees an opening. His foot flies back, he kicks the ball, and it sails into the corner of the goal. Score!

When your team scores a goal everyone feels great, and the crowd cheers. Scoring a goal is the best part of a soccer game.

Shooting: A Different Kind of Passing

Shooting the ball into the goal is just a different kind of passing. The difference between shooting and passing is that a pass goes to a person (your teammate) while a shot is aimed into the goal, away from the other team's goalkeeper.

Young players sometimes think that a shot at the goal must be like a rocket—hit so hard that it puts a hole in the back of the net. Shots need to be strong enough to put the ball in the goal, but they also need to be accurate. When taking a shot, control is just as important as power.

Shooting Moves

When shooting, you use some kinds of passing moves more than others.

Shooting with Your Instep

Most goals are scored from within the penalty box and shots need to be quick, hard, and accurate. These shots are taken with your instep (Figure 7-1) because your instep gives you the power you need to move the ball into the goal quickly. When shooting with your instep, bend slightly at the waist. When you make contact with the ball, kick through the center of the ball (Figure 7-2).

Shooting with the Inside of Your Foot

When you're very close to the goal, and when the goalie is busy on the other side of the goal, or on the ground, shoot with the inside of your foot (Figure 7-3). This will give you a very accurate, but less powerful shot. (The power isn't as important as accuracy in this case, because the goalie is out of the way.)

When you're dribbling in close to the goal and the goalie is moving toward you to block your shot, you can use an inside-of-the-foot shot right from the dribble. You can get the shot off fast, and send it around the goalie (Figure 7-4).

7-1, 7-2: To get maximum power on your shot, you want to strike the ball with your instep. To do this, point your shooting foot down and slightly angled toward the ground (7-1). Attempt to kick the ball with your shoe laces (7-2) and follow through with your kicking leg.

7-3, 7-4: Shooting with the inside of your foot doesn't generate maximum velocity on your kick, but it gives you better accuracy. Keep your shooting foot parallel to the ground, and strike the middle to bottom third of the ball (7-3). The backswing is short (7-4) which allows the offensive player to get his shot off quickly.

Other Shots

You can use any of the passes in Chapter 4 to shoot for a goal. Sometimes a chip shot, a head shot, a one-touch, or even a small tap can be enough to keep the ball away from the goalie and score.

Taking Aim

When taking a shot, aim low, for the edges of the goal. This is because the goalie is usually near the center of the goal. Even though you should shoot for the edges, try to stay away from the upper corners of the goal. They may be tough places for the goalie to reach, but they are also tough places for you to aim for, making it a risky shot. When you shoot for the upper edges of the goal, the ball tends to sail out of bounds above the goal.

Another reason for you to aim low is that it's harder for the goalie to dive than it is for him to jump. It's much easier for him to tip or punch high balls right over the goal and out of bounds.

Wall Target Drill

With colored tape, make two Xs on a wall, about three feet above the ground. Pretend that one of the Xs is the goalie and the other X is a spot at the back of the net. Stand 10 feet from the wall and practice using your instep to shoot the ball at the back of the net. Then pretend that the other X is the back of the net and practice shooting for that X. Practice shooting with both feet.

Shooting Tips

Some important things to remember when shooting are:

- **A quick, powerful kick** gives the goalie less time to get in position to block your shot.

- When shooting with your foot, **your planting foot is very important** because it controls your timing and balance. Plant your foot beside the ball so that your knee is over the ball when you kick it. If you want to loft the ball a little, place your planting foot toward the back of the ball.

- **Don't look at the net.** Keep your eye on the center of the ball when you shoot. If your feet are placed correctly, the ball will go where you aim it.

- **Lean into the kick.**

- Don't kick at the goalie. **Aim for the edges of the goal.**

- **Remember to follow through.**

Shooting with Your Brain

When you pass the ball to a teammate, your brain is tuned to shoot for a target (your teammate). When you shoot for the goal, your mind has a different job to do. You want to aim away from the goalie and into the open spaces of the net (Figure 7-5).

During the game, watch the goalie to see if high balls or low balls are harder for him to block. See if he tends to move one way more than another. You can pick up clues that will help you make a successful shot.

Serving Up Shots Drill

Six or more passers, each with a ball, spread out around the penalty box. One player, who is the shooter, stands in the center. One after another, the passers send their balls to the shooter. The shooter must get the ball under control, then shoot it into the goal, or one-touch the ball into the goal. Passers should send balls to the shooter on the ground, in the air, fast, slow, bouncing, and so on. After the shooter's turn, he trades places with a passer, who becomes the new shooter.

7-5: Always try to aim for the corners when taking a shot on goal. A powerful shot can always be stopped if it's at the goalkeeper, but if it's placed in the corner, he doesn't have a chance.

7-6 through 7-8: When taking shooting practice, always leave some time for striking a moving ball. There is rarely time to set up your shot in the game. Most shots have to be hit first-time. Have a teammate feed you balls and hit them while they're moving.

Shooting Practice

Dribbling the ball toward the goal and taking shots during practice will help you improve your shooting skills, but it won't help you prepare for what it's like to play in a game. The best way to train for a game is to practice shooting at the goal against a goalie while your teammates try to steal the ball from you. Sometimes you can have one or more shooters and a smaller number of defenders. This way the shooters will have more chances to get off a shot. As the shooters improve, add more defenders to make it harder for the shooters.

You can practice shooting even if you're working on another skill, such as corner kicks, or wall passes, by finishing each kick or pass with a shot on the goal (Figures 7-6 through 7-8). This will help train your mind to focus on getting the ball to the goal during a game.

Make It Up, Play It Out

Here's some games that make shooting practice fun.

Four Goals

You need six or more players, a soccer ball, and a field with four goals marked off, one on each side of the field. Make your goals smaller than a regular soccer goal. Divide the players into two teams. Each team has two goals to shoot for. Each player on a team is assigned to guard a certain player on the other team when the other team has the ball. The team with the most goals at the end of the game, wins (shown in diagram below).

One Goal

You need eight or more players, a soccer ball, two goal markers, and a small field with the goal marked off in the middle. You should be able to shoot a ball through the goal from either side of the field. Divide the players into two teams. Each team has half of its players on each side of the field. Players don't cross the center line, but they may pass to their teammates on the other side. Each team tries to score as many goals as they can by shooting the ball through the goal. The team with the most goals is the winner.

This game can get confusing because both teams are shooting for the same goal. If you're not sure which team shot the ball through the goal, it doesn't count.

Knock Out

You need three or more players, a soccer ball, and a wall.

Players get in a line with the first player facing the wall. The first player kicks the ball into the wall, then runs to the end of the line. The second player gets the rebound and kicks the ball into the wall again. The second player runs to the end of the line, and play continues.

How players make an out depends on which shooting skill you want to work on. If you are shooting close to the wall, you may have to kick the ball before it bounces on the ground. If you shoot from farther away, you may have to trap the ball, then kick it. You can draw a line on the wall, and have to shoot the ball above the line.

Once you decide on the rule, any player who fails to keep the rule is out of the game. The last player left is the winner.

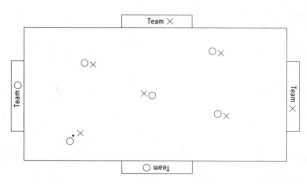

7-9 through 7-13: This player is shown volleying a cross out of the air and into the corner for a goal. Striking the ball first-time often gives your shot its best chance of finding the back of the net. It doesn't allow the defenders any time to block your shot, and it can also catch the goalie out of position.

Keep Focused

1. Shooting is just a different kind of passing except that the ball goes away from a person, not toward a person.
2. A shot doesn't always have to be powerful to make a goal.
3. When shooting with your foot, your planting foot should be beside the ball to keep the shot low.
4. Aim for the edges of the goal.
5. Train your brain to shoot for the empty spaces in the goal and to watch the goalie for clues.
6. Practice shooting into the goal against a goalie while one or two defenders are trying to steal the ball from you.

8

Goalkeeping

I n soccer, the goalkeeper is a very special player. He wears a different uniform than his teammates, and he is the only player on the team who can use his hands on the ball during play. If you're the goalkeeper for your team, your job is to make the save (stop the ball from coming into your team's goal). Because you can use your hands to do this, you need to learn different skills than your teammates.

Special Rules for Goalkeepers

Here are three special rules that apply to goalies:

1. **Use of Hands Rule.** Goalies are allowed to use their hands on the ball when they play inside the penalty area, but when they play outside the penalty area, they become a field player, and can't use their hands on the ball.

2. **Four-Step Rule.** A goalkeeper may not take more than four steps while he's in possession of (has) the ball.

3. **Immunity Rule.** *Immunity* means that while the goalkeeper has possession of the ball, the opponents may not interfere with him in any way.

Are You Ready to Be a Goalie?

While the ability to catch the ball is probably the most important skill for a goalie, you need a certain kind of personality in order to play the position. Goalies need the following five characteristics:

1. **Confidence.** A goalie needs to be able to make a quick decision and take action without stopping to wonder if he's making the right choice.

2. **Mental Toughness.** A goalie has to cover all areas of a very large goal and never, ever stop to think that he would rather not throw his body on the ground to stop a ball.

3. **Leadership.** A goalie has to captain his defensive teammates.

4. **Physical Agility.** A goalie needs to be agile (able to move quickly and easily in any direction with complete control of his body).

5. **Strength.** A goalie must be strong. The strength exercises in Chapter One can help you work on building strength.

Skills for Goalkeeping

Once you've decided that you have the personality to be a goal-keeper, the next step is to learn how to do the job.

Your Position on the Field

As a goalie, you spend most of your time in the penalty area, guarding the goal. When you are within the penalty area, you are allowed to use your hands and arms to touch the ball.

Basic Stance

While you're waiting for the ball, your feet should be about as far apart as your shoulders are. Your knees should be slightly bent, and your weight should be forward on the balls of your feet. This saves time when you have to spring into action quickly. Your

8-1: When the action is on his half of the field, the goaltender should be in the "goalie position" at all times. The legs should about shoulder-width apart with the weight on the balls of your feet. Keep your hands out with the palms up, and bend slightly at the waist. Always keep your eyes on the play.

8-2: For ground shots, go down on one knee and field the ball inside the standing leg. Keep your body behind the ball in case it takes a bad hop.

arms should be at the sides of your body with your elbows bent, hands up, palms facing forward. Keep your thumbs spread out away from your fingers. Your eyes should be watching the ball all the time. Start every move from this basic stance (Figure 8-1).

Getting Behind the Ball

Keeping your body between the ball and the goal is the most important part of your job. If you're in the right place, even if you can't catch the ball, your body might block it from going into the goal. Getting your body behind the ball means your whole body, not just your legs. If the ball is coming in on the ground, you have to get down on one knee to pick up the ball (Figure 8-2). If you just bend over from a standing position, there's much less of your body to stop the ball, especially if your legs are apart.

Using Your Hands

Since you are the one player on your team who can use his hands, you need to use them every chance you get. Many young goalies use their bodies to stop the ball first, then catch it. Or they reach out with a foot to stop the ball, rather than diving for it and catching it in their hands. Don't make these mistakes. Use your hands and arms as much as possible.

8-3: Reach out for the ball and catch it with both hands. Catch it out front so that you still have your body behind the ball in case it slips through your hands.

8-4: If a shot is too high to catch with your hands, punch the ball over the crossbar. Make sure you punch the ball up, and over the goal and not back out into the field of play.

Catching the Ball

Always keep your hands up. When you make a catch, get your thumbs behind the ball (Figure 8-3). This will let the ball give (push against your thumbs) a little and take away some of the power from the ball. Don't try to scoop the ball into your chest. There's no give that way and chances are that you won't be able to hang on to the ball.

Punching the Ball

Sometimes a ball can't be caught because it is out of your reach. When that happens, jump for it and use your hands to punch (push) the ball so it goes wide of the goal or over the top of the goal. Be careful in which direction you punch the ball. The last thing you want to do is punch it out in front of the goal and maybe give the other team a better shot (Figure 8-4).

When you punch the ball out of bounds, you give the other team a chance at a corner shot, but you also give your defense a chance to get in position to stop them.

If there are no attackers right in front of the goal, you can slap the ball down in front of you, but that is the only time you should do this.

Reflex Drill

To be a goalie, you must have good reflexes (fast reactions). You can improve your reflexes by doing this drill every day. You and another goalie kneel down opposite each other about five feet apart. The other goalie throws the ball to you as hard as he can, making sure you will be able to reach the ball. You make the save and throw the ball back to the other goalie, who makes the save and throws back to you. Throw the ball to the right, to the left, low, and high.

Diving

Diving is the hardest skill you need to learn. When you're a goalie, you have to dive on the ground without using your hands to soften your fall. Your hands must be free to catch or punch the ball. A goalkeeper who uses his hands or arms for landing is in trouble. By the time his hands are done breaking his fall, the ball is in the net and the opponent has scored.

Practice Falling Off Your Knees

To learn to how to fall when diving, get down on your knees. This way you won't have so far to fall, and you can practice without being afraid. Use the following steps to practice falling:

1. Get down on your knees and put your weight on one knee.

2. Turn your body in the direction of your weighted knee.

3. Fall off the weighted knee to the side.

4. As you fall, keep your hands up as if you were reaching for the ball.

8-5: A great drill to practice catching the ball with your hands is to dive from your knees. This isolates the hands and forces you to catch the ball cleanly to stop the shot.

Practice Falling Off Your Feet

After you have practiced falling off both knees and to both sides, stand up and fall off your feet. Always fall to the same side as your weighted foot. Remember to keep your hands up as you fall.

Practice Diving for the Ball

After you are comfortable falling off your feet, it's time to practice with the ball. Get another player to pass the ball to you. Now you have to do more than just fall off your weighted foot. You have to *dive* (push) off. If all you do is fall over, you may land short of the ball and miss the catch. Here's how to make the dive:

1. Put your weight on the foot that is closest to the ball.

2. Turn your body toward the ball.

3. Dive off your weighted foot in the direction of the ball.

4. As you fall, your lower hand should be directly in the path of the ball and your upper hand should be ready to grab the top of the ball. (Your thumbs should almost be touching so that your hands make a pocket for the ball.)

5. As soon as you catch the ball, bring it against your chest and curl your body around it.

When you practice diving for the ball, have the passer send the ball to your left and to your right. Once in a while, have him send you some balls that you can catch while standing up, so you get a rest from diving.

Off-the-Knees Diving Drill

This drill lets you practice diving for the ball without hitting the ground real hard. You and another goalie kneel down opposite each other about eight feet apart. The other goalie rolls the ball to you, just a little out of your reach. Fall off your knees to make the save (Figure 8-5). Then get back on your knees and send the ball back to the other goalie. Roll the ball to the right sometimes, and to the left other times.

Narrowing the Angle to Avoid Diving

Since it's much easier to catch a ball standing up than it is to catch one while diving, try to figure out what angle (path) the ball will be taking to the goal. Then you can move to the right place to catch the ball while staying on your feet. For example, if the ball is coming from the right, move toward that side of the goal (Figure 8-6).

If an attacker is coming at you, one-on-one, move off the goal line. The closer you are to the attacker, the narrower the shooting angle becomes. Don't rush toward the attacker until you are sure you will get the ball. Otherwise the attacker can pass the ball to his teammate, who can send it in the other side of the net.

After the Save

After you save the ball, you have to get it back to your teammates. There are two ways to do this. You can throw it with your hands, or *punt* it (kick it down the field as far as you can) (Figures 8-7 through 8-9).

Whether you throw or punt the ball, make sure that you move it out to the sideline instead of down the center of the field.

How do you know when to throw and when to punt? Look at your teammates. If one of them is wide open on the side, throw the ball to him. If there's no one open in throwing range, then it's better to punt, because it will get the ball farther away from your goal. You don't want to throw the ball only to have it stolen and come right back at the goal (Figure 8-10).

Rapid Fire Drill

This drill is good for building your endurance. It also helps you sharpen your goalie skills. All players, except for you, line up along the top of the penalty box. They each have a soccer ball. You are defending the goal. The first player takes a shot. When the ball has almost reached the goal, the next person takes a shot, and so on. The shooters have to have good timing in taking their shots. They don't want to give you much time to recover from each shot, but they can't fire all the balls at once, or you won't be able to save any of them. The first time through this drill, the shooters should aim for you. This way, you can warm up by making contact with every ball without having to fly all over the place. Once you're warmed up, the shooters aim at the edges of the goal.

8-6: Notice how far the goalie is out of the net (8-10). If the offensive player is about to shoot from a specific area of the field, move out and cut down the angle so he has a smaller target to shoot at.

Special Situations

After you are good at basic goalkeeping skills, you need to learn about special situations that can come up during a game. In foul situations you will have to guard against corner kicks, direct kicks, and indirect kicks. After the ball goes out of bounds, you'll have to guard against the throw-in. Make sure you know where to stand and where your team's defensive players should stand in order to best block the goal in each case.

For corner kicks, you should stand on the far post, because it's easier to move in to catch the ball than it is to move backward. For direct kicks, you should line up your defensive players into a wall in front of the goal, with their outside shoulder closing off one side of the goal. That way the kicker can only go around the wall in one direction, and it's your job to guard that side.

There are times during a game when you need to leave the penalty area and play on the field. Be sure to take some time during every team practice to play on the field. Playing on the field teaches you how your defense moves to stop an attack.

8-7 through 8-9: Often goalkeepers will use a drop kick instead of a punt. Drop the ball and just after it hits the ground, strike the ball on its way up. Goalies use this method because they can use a bigger backswing, and get better distance on their kick.

Learning what players and which areas of your goal your defense covers helps you know what to do when you are playing in the penalty area. Playing the field also makes you more aware of problems with your defense and what adjustments should be made. Playing the field makes you a better captain of your team's defense.

Even though you need different skills than your teammates, you still want to practice with them. Spend part of each practice session working on your own special skills, and the rest of the practice time working with your team. When you practice with your team, everyone feels more like they are playing in a game. You get practice guarding the goal, and your teammates get practice dribbling, passing, and shooting. You may be great at catching the ball, but your skill won't do you much good if you haven't learned where to stand while the ball is coming down the field. Playing the game is the best way to learn goalie skills.

8-10: If a teammate is open a short distance away, you may want to throw him the ball. Use the windmill throw for best accuracy and velocity.

8-11: In the rapid fire drill, shooters line up from about 12 yard-line. The first player from one end shoots, and is followed immediately by the next player in line. The drills ends when all players have shot. It's a great way for the goalie to practice quickness and reaction time.

8-12: If you come out to break up a play, make sure you come out strong. If you're hesitant, it could result in a goal scored against you and your teammates.

Make It Up, Play It Out

Goalie is a great game to play when you don't have a lot of room.

Goalie

You need two to four players, a soccer ball, a wall or small area, and markers such as colored tape for the wall, or caps, cones, or flags for the area. Mark off a goal area on the wall or ground. Then mark off a boundary line about eight feet from the goal.

One player, who is the goalie, stands in front of the goal area and tries to keep the ball from going into the goal.

The other players take turns staying behind the boundary and trying to shoot the ball past the goalie. If a player gets the ball past the goalie, he gets one point. If the goalie makes a save, he throws the ball back out to the player who must kick it before it stops moving. If the kicker misses the ball, the goalie gets one point. After each shooter has 10 tries, one of the players becomes the goalie, and the goalie becomes a shooter. The player with the most points at the end of the game is the winner.

Keep Focused

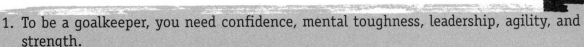

1. To be a goalkeeper, you need confidence, mental toughness, leadership, agility, and strength.
2. Get your body behind the ball.
3. Use your hands to catch the ball and keep your thumbs behind the ball while catching it.
5. Knock the ball out of bounds, not in front of the goal.
6. A goalie must dive without using his arms or hands to break his fall.
7. Learn to dive by practicing falling off your knees.
8. Use a punt or a throw to get rid of the ball after you save it.
9. Narrow your angle by shifting your position.
10. Play the field to understand your defense.
11. A goalkeeper needs to practice alone and with his team.

9

Strategy: Putting It All Together

very player on a team needs to know the basic skills of dribbling, passing, receiving, heading, and shooting. But it still takes more to win a game. A winning team needs a very special something, called strategy. Strategy means getting the better of the other team by out-thinking them. A team with a winning strategy knows exactly what moves to make, when to make them, and why those moves work.

Playing Positions

Your coach knows the strengths and weaknesses of all the players on your team. He uses that information in deciding on a strategy for each game. That strategy includes who plays what position. There are 11 players on a soccer team, but there are only four basic playing positions. Except for the goalie, the number of players in each of the other positions during a game depends on the team strategy. The positions are:

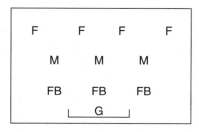

Fullbacks

The fullbacks (also called defenders), defend their team's goal from attack. If the fullbacks do their jobs perfectly, the goalie doesn't ever have to make a save. The fullbacks *mark* men (try to keep an attacker from receiving the ball). They also *intercept* the ball (trap it when the other team passes or loses control), *block* attackers (keep them from moving the ball down the field), and *tackle* (take the ball away from the other team).

Forwards

The main job of the forwards is to put the ball in the goal. Forwards need to be great shooters, fast dribblers, and expert headers.

Midfielders

The midfielders (also called halfbacks), are the links (connections) between the fullbacks and the forwards. Midfielders *coordinate* the play by moving up, down, and across the field, sometimes attacking, sometimes defending, depending on how they are needed. Midfielders need to be expert passers and strong runners.

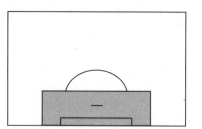

The Goalkeeper

There is only one goalie. His job is to stop the ball from coming into his team's goal. He usually plays in the penalty area and he is the only player who can use his hands on the ball during play. The goalie can play outside the penalty area, too, but then he becomes a field player and can't use his hands on the ball. A goalie must have all the skills of a field player, plus he must be an expert at catching the ball with his hands.

Doing All the Jobs

Even though each position has certain jobs to do, every player should consider himself to be both an attacker and a defender. For example, if you are a fullback, and you steal the ball from an opponent, you should then consider yourself to be an attacker and get in the best position to help attack the goal. If you are a forward, and the other team steals the ball from you, don't just stand there feeling bad. Become a defender and go after the opponent with everything you've got.

Offensive Strategies

Even though the coach decides the strategy for the game, the players have to make some strategy decisions during the game. Here's some strategies to use when your team is on the attack:

1. **When you're in the opponent's half of the field, get the ball to the center.** From the center of the field, you have more passing and shooting choices, and it's harder for the opponents to cut off your shooting angle.

2. **Spread the opponent's defense.** If you and your teammates stay spread out from each other, the defense will have to cover a much bigger area of the field, making their job harder.

3. **Support the player in front of you.** If you're a fullback or a midfielder, don't think your job is over once you've passed the ball to your forward. Stay behind him and let him know you're there. He may need to pass the ball back to you. (There's more about support later in this chapter.)

4. **Switch sides of the field.** If all the play has been on one side of the field for a while, try moving the ball to the other side. This will cause the opponent's entire defense to shift, and it may give you an opening.

When the other team has the ball, all your efforts should go toward protecting the goal. Here's some defensive strategies your team might use in a game:

Zone and Player-to-Player Defense

There are two different styles of defense: zone and player-to-player. Your coach may decide to use either one or both during a game.

Zone

When you are on *zone* defense, you are assigned to cover a certain area of the field and your job is to *mark* any player (keep him from getting the ball) that comes into that area.

Player-to-Player

When you are on *player-to-player* defense, you are assigned to mark a certain opponent, staying with him, no matter where he goes on the field.

Marking a Player

When marking your opponent, stay between him and the goal. You also want to stay between him and the ball if you can do so without giving up protecting the goal (Figure 9-1).

You don't have to be on top of your opponent all the time. The farther he is from the ball, the farther you can be from him. When you are far away from him, you are able to help out a teammate if his attacker happens to break away from him.

If the man you are marking gets the ball, move in close and apply *high pressure* (bother him). Bother him so much that he can't look up to see what his passing options are. Push him toward the corner of the field. Not only will you be going away from the goal, but the sideline and the endline will stop him from passing in those two directions.

9-1: When playing man to man defense, it's your job to stay with your man wherever he goes. Try to match up with a player who is comparable to your size and speed.

Tackling

Every player needs to know how to tackle (steal the ball from an attacker). The best times to tackle are when the opponent has just received the ball and doesn't yet have it under control or when he pushes it forward while dribbling (Figure 9-2).

While you are waiting for your chance to tackle, you want to *jockey* (stay with the attacker). Jockey at an angle to him to force him in the direction you want him to go. While jockeying, keep your knees bent a little and stay on the balls of your feet so you can change direction quickly. Keep your eyes on the ball, and watch for your chance to tackle. There are four basic tackles:

1. **Block tackle.** Watch the opponent dribble and guess when he's going to move his foot forward again. When he does, kick the ball with the inside of your foot at the same time.

2. **Poke Tackle.** Instead of using the inside of your foot to kick the ball, use your toes to poke the ball away from the opponent (Figure 9-3).

3. **Shoulder Charge.** When you are running beside the opponent, lean into him and bump him with your *shoulder* to knock him off balance. Then quickly go after the ball. The shoulder charge is the *only* time during a game that you can touch another player with

9-2: Two opposing players meeting the ball at the same time is called a "stick". Keep your leg firm, weight forward, and kick through the ball.

9-3: A poke tackle is useful when the offensive player is dribbling the ball slowly. Lean back and try to flick the ball away to slow him down. Don't try this when he's moving fast because if you miss he'll blow right past you.

your body. Be careful not to touch him with your hands or arms, or it's a foul. You may use the shoulder charge *only* when you have been jockeying close to the opponent. You can't run at him from a distance before taking a shoulder charge.

4. **Sliding Tackle.** When you aren't able to use any of the first three tackles, a sliding tackle might work. This is a tricky tackle and timing is very important. Come at your opponent from an angle. Bend one knee and drop to the ground on that knee, keeping your other leg straight out in front of you. Use your arm (next to your bent leg) to help soften your *slide* along the ground. Slide in front of your opponent and kick the ball away from him. There are two reasons why sliding is your last choice when tackling. If you trip your opponent while sliding, you may get a penalty for kicking or tripping. If you miss the tackle, then your opponent still has the ball and you are on the ground, leaving him in the clear (Figures 9-4 and 9-5).

Support

Support strategy means that you and your teammates help each other out. You need to give support when:

- **You are nearest your teammate when he tries to steal the ball and fails.** When this happens, the attacker dribbles on toward the goal, while your teammate is left behind, looking

9-4, 9-5: Use the slide tackle only in desparate situations. Slide in from the side with your lead leg extended to swipe the ball (9-4). You must make contact with the ball. If you only hit the player's legs, you'll be called for a foul.

foolish. Support your teammate by moving in on the attacker. As soon as your teammate recovers, he marks the man you left open.

- **You're at least two passes away from the ball.** This means that the player you're marking is not in a position to receive a pass at the time. When that's the case, you should be helping protect the middle of the field. Even if your teammate is putting high pressure on the ball handler, you can help him by cutting off passing options.

If you find yourself facing two opponents and you aren't getting any support from your teammates, the best thing to do is hold off, giving your teammates a chance to help you. If you go ahead and chose one opponent to guard, the other one will have an open path to the goal.

Formations

Not only does your coach use strategy to decide who plays which position during the game, he also uses strategy to decide which *formations* his team will use on the field. A formation is the way the players are arranged on the field—who plays where.

The coach gives the formation to his players before the game, but he can change it during the game, depending on what's happening on the field. In youth league soccer, the coach usually signals a change of formation to his team. In college and professional games, the goalkeeper gives the formation to the players on the field.

All formations include some number of fullbacks, some number of midfielders, and some number of forwards. The goal-

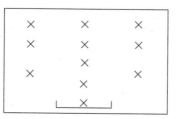

4-3-3 Formation

keeper is never mentioned in the formation. Here's two basic formations that your coach might use:

WM Formation

The *WM formation* is one of the most basic formations used in Youth League soccer. It's called the WM because when the players line up on the field, they form a W and a M. The W is formed by two inside players, two sideline players, and a forward. Three fullbacks and two midfielders form the M. The WM formation is used for playing both offense and defense.

Four-Two-Four Formation

In this formation, four offensive players spread out across the field in a line. Behind them, are two midfielders. Behind the midfielders, are four defensive players. This formation is clearly weak in the middle, but it can work well if your team has two strong midfielders in top physical shape. They have to link your team's offense and defense and they have a lot of territory to cover. The advantage of this formation is that it allows you to put more players on both your offense and your defense.

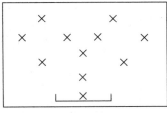

4-4-2 Formation

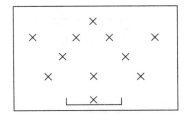

WM Formation

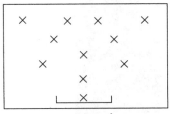

4-2-4 Formation

Make It Up, Play It Out

The following just-for-fun games can help you practice for the real thing.

Square Soccer

You need four or more players, a soccer ball, a small, square playing area, and markers such as caps, cones, or flags. Mark off the corners of the square. Players divide up into two teams and stand along the edges of the square. Each team is responsible for two sides of the square. Players don't go into the center of the square, but kick the ball through the square to get it over the other team's sides. If the ball does leaves the square, then the team who is not defending that side gets a point. The first team to get 15 points, wins. If many people are playing, more soccer balls can be added to make the game harder.

Outside the Lines

ATTACK! ATTACK!
In the early years of soccer, before the rules were written down, the most popular formation was no goalie, two defensemen, and nine attackers!

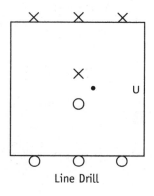

Line Drill

Line Soccer

You need eight or more players, a soccer ball, a referee, and a field with two parallel boundary lines marked off across the center. Players divide into two teams. Each team stands behind one of the boundary lines, so the two teams are facing each other across an empty area. Each team gives every player a number, starting with the number, one. This means that each team will have a number one, a number, two, and so on.

The referee (someone who isn't a player) calls out one or more numbers and throws the ball into the empty area between the boundary lines. The players, whose numbers are called, rush into the area and try to get the ball across the opponent's line. This will be like a game of one-on-one or two-on-two.

The players, whose numbers aren't called, stand on their boundary line. They can't leave the line but they can block any tries to get the ball over their line as long as they don't use their hands or arms.

A team who gets the ball over the opponent's line, scores a point. When a point is scored, the players go back to their lines and the referee calls out different numbers. Sometimes the referee calls out new numbers in the middle of play. When this happens, any players in the middle whose numbers are called may continue to kick the ball. Any players in the middle whose numbers aren't called have to leave the ball and go back to their line while the new numbers come out to do battle. The team with the most points at the end of the game is the winner.

Keep Focused

1. A winning team needs a winning strategy.
2. The fullback's primary responsibility is to defend the goal, the forward's is to attack, and the midfielder's is to link the fullbacks and the forwards.
3. Every player should be both an attacker and a defender.
4. When you're attacking, spread the opponent's defense by staying away from your teammates.
5. Defense strategies can be either zone or player-to-player
6. When marking your opponent, stay between him and the goal.
7. If you're marking a player who has the ball, force him to the sideline.
8. Every player needs to know how to tackle.
9. Support your teammates whether you're on offense or on defense.
10. Your coach decides which formations your team uses during a game.

CHAPTER 10

Restarts

When the ball goes out of bounds, play stops. Someone gets the blame for having touched the ball last, the other team gets the ball, and there's a *restart* (play starts again). Play also stops when a foul has been committed so a penalty can be taken. This chapter will fill you in on the different kinds of restarts that are used in soccer.

Throw-In

You already know that in soccer, players (except for the goalie) can't use their hands on the ball. There is one exception to this rule. When the ball has been knocked out of bounds over the sideline, a player from the team that didn't touch the ball last throws the ball back in bounds with his hands. The player who is making the *throw-in* gets the ball on the sideline where the ball went out of bounds (Figures 10-1 through 10-3). When throwing the ball back into bounds, you must:

- Use both hands equally.
- Bring the ball straight over your head in a straight line before releasing it.

10-1 through 10-3: When throwing the ball in, bring the ball straight back over your head with both hands (10-1). Throw the ball forward (back over your head) using both hands equally to avoid an illegal spin. Follow through with your arms, and keep both feet on the ground (10-3). If your feet come up, you'll be called for a foul throw.

- Release the ball while it is still over your head.
- Keep both feet on the ground at the moment the ball is released.

Outside the Lines

THROW-IN TRICKS

The rule that says you have to have both feet on the ground when releasing the ball on a throw-in makes it hard to put any power behind the throw. Players have come up with a few tricks to get more power while still obeying the rules. One trick is to take a running start, then drag the top of one foot along the ground while releasing the ball. Players have even done flips in order to throw with more power!

Throw-in Strategies

There's no referee's signal that tells you when to throw the ball in bounds. If you throw it in immediately, you can sometimes catch the other team off guard.

Don't just throw the ball onto the field. Throw it to one of your teammates. A throw-in is a free pass and you don't want to waste it. Your teammates should be moving around on the field, trying to get free. Throw the ball at their feet because it will be easier for them to get it under control. You can also throw the ball ahead of a teammate down the sideline.

Sometimes the opposing team may forget to mark you after you release the ball. That's a perfect time for the player who receives your throw-in to pass the ball right back to you.

If the other team is making the throw-in, your team's players want to mark the opponents as quickly as possible, including the inbounder (player making the throw-in). Be aware of balls heading down the sideline.

One Final Rule

A goal cannot be scored from a throw-in.

Goal Kick

If the attacking team kicks the ball over the defending team's endline, then the defending team gets a goal kick. The ball is placed in the same half of the defending team's goal area where it went out of bounds. If you're the player making the goal kick, use this kick to pass the ball to a teammate. Unless a teammate is wide open near the goal, pass the ball to a wing (sideline player) as far down the field as possible. You don't want to help the attacking team by kicking the ball into the middle of the field (Figure 10-4).

If the defending team kicks the ball over their own endline, then the attacking team gets a corner kick. This is a **free kick** (without interference from the other team) taken from the corner of the field on the side of the goal where the ball went out.

If you're the player making the corner kick, kick the ball right in front of the goal. That way the defending team can't cut off any angle of attack. You will probably need to loft the ball, because the defending team will probably have a player ready to intercept a ball on the ground (Figure 10-5). Some players put spin on the ball when kicking it from the corner, so that the ball will turn in, toward the goal. (Chapter 2, Passing, tells you how to put spin on the ball.)

If you're receiving or defending on a corner kick, you want to get your head in the way of the ball. There will be a crowd in front of the goal and there won't be time for the ball to drop to the ground. The first head to get to the ball will decide its direction.

10-4: Goal kicks are primarily used to clear the ball out of the defensive end. Keep the ball away from the middle of the field in case of a mis-kick.

Direct Kicks

When a foul is committed, the fouled team gets a direct kick. This is a free kick, taken from the spot where the foul occurred. Until the ball is kicked, defenders and receivers must stay at least 10 yards from the ball (Figure 10-6).

10-5: Corner kicks are excellent opportunities for the offense to score goals. The kicker should lift the ball near the goal mouth, but far enough so it's out of the goalkeeper's reach.

10-6: On a direct kick that's within scoring distance, the shooter has several options. He can attempt to shoot the ball at, or over the wall of players (near post). He can try to shoot the ball past the goalkeeper (far post), or he can pass off to an open teammate. Most good teams have set plays for this situation.

The faster you make this kick, the more advantage you'll have over the other team. The kick can be a pass or a shot on the goal, but it cannot be a dribble (someone else must touch the ball before you can touch it a second time).

If the foul takes place within reach of the goal, many defending teams like to set up a wall to help keep the ball from the goal. To make a wall, four or five players stand shoulder-to-shoulder about 10 yards from the ball. They block off a part of the goal and make the goalkeeper's job a little easier.

Indirect Kicks

When a player breaks certain rules, such as making a dangerous kick, the other team gets an indirect kick. Indirect means that the ball cannot be shot directly into the goal. It must be touched by another player first.

If you are making an indirect kick for your team, and you are near the other team's goal, make the kick a short pass to a teammate who can shoot for the goal. One problem with this move is that the defense can run into play as soon as the ball is kicked, giving them a chance to block your teammate's shot.

Because the ball must be passed to another player on an indirect kick, most defending teams don't set up a wall to block the kick. Instead, they mark up tightly and hope to get to the ball before the shot is taken.

Penalty Kicks

When the defending team fouls in their own penalty area, and the foul is one that calls for a free kick, the attacking team gets a penalty kick (Figure 10-7). A penalty kick is always taken from the penalty line, directly in front of the defending team's goal. The penalty kick is a contest between the kicker and the goalie, who must stand with both his heels on the endline until the ball is kicked. All other players must stay out of the penalty area and at least 10 yards away from the ball. A penalty kicks often results in a goal.

10-7

If you're making the penalty kick for your team, try to kick the ball into the goal, away from the goalie. Make it a low kick because low balls are harder for the goalie to save than high ones. Don't miss the goal.

Penalty Kick Drill

Each player has a ball. Players take turns shooting from the penalty line in front of the goal. If a player misses the goal, he runs after the ball. If he catches it before it stops rolling, he can stay in the drill, otherwise he's out. The drill ends when all players are out. This drill can be done with or without a goalie.

10-7: The easiest way to score on a penalty kick is to aim low for the corners of the goal. In this photo the kicker tries to go up the middle and is denied by the goalie.

Make It Up, Play It Out

Cone Ball is a fun game that helps you practice aiming for the goal.

Cone Ball

You need four players, a soccer ball, a playing area that is a circle, and a cone. Place the cone in the center of the circle. Three players stand around the outside of the circle and one player stands inside the circle with the cone. The person inside the circle defends the cone. Players on the outside of the circle have to keep the ball away from the defender and yet, hit the cone. They pass the ball back and forth across the circle until one

10-8: Restarts are often the direct result of a foul called on a player. 10-8 displays two players with their elbows up which often draws a whistle from referees.

10-9: Just as restarts present scoring opportunities on offense, they can be dangerous when you're on the defensive end. Here (10-9) these defensive players are shown setting up for an incoming corner kick.

of them sees a chance to take a shot at the cone. If the player taking the shot hits the cone, he gets one point and takes a turn defending the cone. If the defender steals the ball, he trades places with the player who last touched it. The player with the most points at the end of the game is the winner.

Keep Focused

1. Throw-ins, goal kicks, and corner kicks are different ways of inbounding the ball on restarts.
2. When making a throw-in, use both hands above your head and keep both feet on the ground.
3. Use a throw-in like a free pass. Make sure you get the ball to a teammate.
4. Goal kicks should go wide to the side.
5. Corner kicks should go to the center.
6. A head ball is the best move for receiving a corner kick.
7. Direct kicks, indirect kicks, and penalty kicks are used when one team commits a foul.
8. To defend against a direct kick, set up a human wall.
9. When making an indirect kick, pass the ball to a teammate.
10. A goal is often scored from a penalty kick.

Glossary

Back pass—The passer steps over the ball, then passes it backward.

Block tackle—Stealing the ball from the attacker by kicking it with your foot at the same time that he kicks it.

Boot—to kick the ball lightly.

Breakaway—When a player breaks away from the opponents and is in the clear.

Center circle—A circle, 10 yards in diameter, in the middle of the soccer field where kickoffs take place.

Center line—The center line cuts across the length of the field and divides it in half.

Chip—A very short pass through the air.

Circuit training—A series of different exercises done, one right after another, at different spots on the field.

Coach—The team's leader and teacher who runs the practice sessions and plans the strategy for the game.

Corner kick—If the ball is knocked out of bounds by a defensive player, a member of the attacking team restarts the play by kicking the ball from the corner closest to where it went out of bounds.

Cut—A quick change of direction.

Dangerous play—Play which can cause injuries such as kicking the ball above chest height.

Defender—**1.** A playing position. Also called a fullback. **2.** A player on the defensive team.

Defense—When the other team has the ball, then you are playing defense and your team is the defending team.

Direct kick—A kick that is allowed to be shot directly into the goal.

Diving header—Diving off your feet toward the ball in order to hit it with your head while your body is in the air.

Dribbling—Ball handling. Moving the ball with the feet.

Drop kick—When the ball comes through the air and bounces once before you send it back through the air. Also called the half volley.

Endlines—There are two endlines, one at each end of the field. If the ball goes over the endline during a game, it is out of bounds.

Fake—To move your body in a way that fools the opponents.

Fancy footwork—Quickly changing from one dribbling style to another in order to keep the ball away from the defender.

Field players—Fullbacks, midfielders, and forwards are called field players because they play on the field. A goalkeeper can become a field player when he leaves the goal area to play on the field.

FIFA—Federation of International Football Associations.

Formation—The arrangement of the players on the field.

Forward—A playing position. Forwards shoot the ball into the goal.

Foul—To break a rule. Also called a violation.

Four-two-four—A formation with four offensive players in the front, two midfielders in the middle, and four defenders in the rear.

Free kick—The player gets to kick the ball without interference from the other team.

Fullback—A playing position. Fullbacks defend their team's goal from attack and steal the ball from the opponents. Also called a defender.

Goal—A wood or metal framework that is 24 feet wide by eight feet high and covered by nets. There are two goals, one at each end of the field.

Goalkeeper—- A position. The goalkeeper guards his team's goal. He wears a different uniform that the rest of his team, and he is the only player who can catch the ball with his hands. Also called a goalie.

Goalmouth—The wide opening of the nets at the front of the goal.

Goal area—A six yard by 20 yard area in front of the goal.

Goal kick—A kick by a member of the defensive team, taken from their own goal area in order to restart the game after the attacking team has kicked the ball out of bounds over the defensive team's goal line.

Halfback—A playing position. Also called a midfielder.

Goal line—The part of the endline that runs across the front of the goal.

Heading—Using the head to hit the ball.

Heading backward—Keeping the ball in the air by using your head to flick it backward.

High kicking—Kicking the ball above chest height, which is against the rules.

Indirect kick—A kick that is not allowed to send the ball directly into the goal. The ball must be first touched by another player before it can be shot at the goal.

Inside-of-the-foot pass—A pass made with the inside of the foot.

Instep—The top of the foot, where your shoelaces are.

Instep pass—A pass made with the instep of the foot.

Jockeying—Staying with an attacker.

Juggling—Keeping the soccer ball up in the air by using any part of the body except the hands and arms.

Kickoff—A kick begins each half of the game and is used after a goal has been scored to put the ball back into play. The ball is placed on the center spot and the kicking team starts the play by kicking the ball toward the opponent's goal.

Linespeople—Game officials who watch the sidelines during play and throw flags to show when a ball is out of bounds.

Loft—To send the ball into the air.

Lofted pass—A pass through the air.

Marking—Keeping an attacker from receiving the ball from his teammate.

Midfielder—A playing position. Midfielders move up, down, and across the field, sometimes attacking, sometimes defending, depending on how they are needed. Also called a halfback.

Offense—When your team has the ball, then you are playing offense and your team is the attacking team.

Offside—When a player is in his attacking half of the field and he fails to keep either the ball or two opponents between himself and the goal.

One-touch pass—When the ball is passed to you and you touch it once, sending it on to a teammate. The one-touch pass is used when you don't have time to get the ball under control before passing it.

Out of bounds—When the ball goes over a sideline or endline.

Outside-of-the-foot pass—A pass made with the outside of the foot.

Overlap—When the attacking team uses one of their defenders as an extra pass receiver.

Pass—Sending the ball from one player to another without using the hands or arms.

Penalty kick—A kick by a member of the attacking team, taken from the penalty spot in front of the defending team's goal after the defending team has committed a foul in its own penalty box.

Penalty box—A rectangle in front of the goal area that is 44 yards by 18 yards.

Penalty spot—A spot inside the penalty box located opposite the center of the goal and 12 yards from the goal line.

Player-to-player defense—A defensive strategy in which each member of the defensive team is assigned a certain member of the attacking team, staying with him, no matter where he goes on the field.

Poke tackle—Using the toes to poke the ball away from an attacker.

Poor conduct—Bad behavior by a player during a game, such as waving a hand in an opponent's face.

Punch—When a goalkeeper hits the ball with his hand to send it up in the air and away from the goal.

Receiver—A player who receives a pass.

Referee—One of three game officials. The referee is in charge of the field. He starts and stops play during the game.

Rock and roll—Rocking the body to one side, then moving in the opposite direction in order to fool an opponent.

Shooting—Using any part of the body except hands and arms to try to send the ball into the opponent's goal.

Shoulder Charge—Bumping an opponent with your shoulder to knock him off balance.

Sidelines—There are two sidelines, one on each side of the field. If the ball goes over the sideline during a game, it is out of bounds.

Sliding tackle—Going down on one knee and sliding on the ground toward an opponent in order to kick the ball away from him.

Square—A pass that goes directly out to the side of the field.

Strategy—**1.** Getting the better of the other team by out-thinking them. **2.** The game plan.

Stutter step—A quick stop followed by a quick start.

Tackle—Use the feet to take the ball away from an opponent.

Throw-in—When a ball goes out of bounds over the sideline, it is thrown back into play from the spot where it went out by a member of the team that did not touch it last. The throw-in must be from above the player's head, using both hands while both feet are touching the ground.

Trapping—Getting the ball under control by using the feet.

Volley—When the ball is passed through the air to you from a teammate and you pass it back without letting it touch the ground.

Wall pass—A pass in which the passer bounces the ball of a teammate, sprints around a defensive player, and receives the ball again. Also called the give and go, or the one-two pass.

Wing—**1.** The part of the field near the sideline. **2.** A player near the sideline.

Wing pass—A sideline pass.

W M formation—A formation in which the players are arranged on the field in the shape of a W and a M.

Zone defense—A defensive strategy in which each member of the defensive team is assigned to defend a certain area of the field, marking any player who comes into that area.

Index